# THE PRIVATE LIFE OF
# HENRY MAITLAND

GEORGE GISSING
*at the age of 44*

*Morley Roberts*

# THE PRIVATE LIFE OF
# HENRY MAITLAND

*A Portrait of George Gissing*

*Edited, with an Introduction, by*
MORCHARD BISHOP

*LONDON*
THE RICHARDS PRESS
*ROYAL OPERA ARCADE*
*PALL MALL*

LONDON : THE RICHARDS PRESS LTD
MARTIN SECKER : DIRECTOR
1958

# Note

"*The Private Life of Henry Maitland*"
*was first published by Eveleigh Nash in 1912;
it was re-issued with certain revisions in 1923
by Nash & Grayson Ltd.*

# Introduction

## (1)

ARLY in the summer of 1912, Frank Swinnerton, who had been commissioned by Mr. Martin Secker to write a book on George Gissing, applied for information to Morley Roberts, who was known to have been Gissing's oldest friend. To this application, Roberts replied with a flat refusal, for which, however, he advanced, with due courtesy, two reasons. The first was " that the time has not come when the truth could be told without troubling others unduly ", the second, " that I am using all I know of him in a book for future publication as it stands, or for immediate publication as a mere story with other names in it." Swinnerton, who had received from Gissing's other well-known literary friend, H. G. Wells, a response equally courteous but almost equally discouraging, did a valiant best with the materials that were available to him, and in the autumn of that same year his book, *George Gissing : a Critical Study*, appeared. Within the very week of its publication there came forth from the firm of Eveleigh Nash a work which bore the superficial aspect of a novel and had for title *The Private Life of Henry Maitland* : Morley Roberts's name was upon its title page, though he there claimed to be no more than the editor of " A Record dictated by J. H. [1] "

This book at once created something of a sensation ; but though it was praised in a few places, comment upon it, on the whole, was adverse. No one who had the most cursory acquaintance with the literature of the two preceding decades could have had the slightest doubt of what Roberts had done : he had produced a veiled portrait of Gissing in which the veils were so transparent that they hid nothing, and he had at the same time, by allowing his book to bear the outward semblance of a work of fiction, deprived it of any pretension to authority. The facts of Gissing's career, as he related them, were so tragic, and at the same time to the majority of readers so

[1] J. H. is of course Roberts himself.

entirely unknown, that the general opinion at the time seems to have been that he had butchered his friend's reputation to make a catchpenny melodrama. One of the few critics who did not take this view was Swinnerton himself, who, with exceptional generosity in the circumstances, gave the book a very favourable notice in *The Bookman*. This review elicited a further letter from Morley Roberts, who on December 9 sent to Swinnerton to thank him : " Considering what has been said of me [he wrote] I think it noble of you to say what you do. . . . Whatever is said (and I hear more is to be said) I shall not open my mouth. If the book isn't a defence— what can I say ? " Furthermore, he expressed his deep regret for the cavalier fashion in which he had responded to Swinnerton's earlier request for information, and, in an attempt to justify it, he added : " When you wrote, I was writing this book in a state near to madness."

Many years afterwards, in his *Background with Chorus* (1956), Swinnerton advanced the proposition that Roberts was spurred on by his approach to begin *Henry Maitland*. Roberts himself, in the passage quoted, implies that he had already begun it when Swinnerton's letter came to hand. The point is now hardly capable of solution, nor is it perhaps of much moment. The chief reason why I have (thanks to the courtesy of Mr. Swinnerton) made use here of this correspondence is because I think Morley Roberts's phrase about writing his book " in a state near to madness " important ; for madness and what is called inspiration are generally supposed to be conditions closely akin, and it seems to me that *Henry Maitland* is still, after the lapse of some five-and-forty years, a book that bears unmistakably the stamp of inspiration.

Consider the facts : Gissing was born on November 22, 1857, and Morley Roberts just a month later, on December 29, 1857, so that last year saw the centenary of both their births. Gissing had died in 1903, at the age of forty-six ; and by 1912 Morley Roberts was already fifty-five years of age. The two had first met at Owens College, in Manchester, about 1873, and had been lifelong friends thereafter. But by 1912 Gissing had been dead nine years, and what Roberts then set himself to do (whether spurred on by Swinnerton's request or independently) was to draw a life-sized portrait of the man that he had known. I use the word portrait advisedly, for I think it crucial : *Henry Maitland* is largely a static book, an essay in impressionism, in which events are recorded far less for their own sake than for the part they play in building up the total effect. The passage which Roberts quotes, at the beginning of his third chapter, from Boswell's *Tour to the Hebrides*, is therefore worth repeating, for it seems to contain the very germ from which his book sprang : " Talking of biography, he [Johnson] said he did not think the life of any literary man in England had been well written. Besides the common incidents of life it should tell us his studies, his mode of living, the means by which he attained to excellence, and his opinion of his own works." Such was the goal at which Roberts aimed, and few who read him now, in the light of the later knowledge that we have of Gissing, can doubt that he achieved it. He had, in fact, achieved a small masterpiece, conceived in affection but disfigured by no touch of sentimentality. Even its humour is sound ; for smile as we may at Gissing's valetudinarian outcries, our smile is that of affection, not of scorn. Besides, quite apart from the great interest of its subject-matter, the book in its execution is strikingly original ; one is indeed tempted to say that it is unique, since one cannot call to mind anything in the same way that at all resembles it.

In 1912, however, it must have worn an uncommonly different look, for its true excellences were then gravely obscured by the fictional draperies that encumbered it : draperies, moreover, that merely irritated the instructed, since in fact they impeded without concealing. Roberts, in his first letter to Swinnerton, had spoken of " a book for future publication as it stands ", and no doubt the ideal solution would have been for him to have waited for this future publication, and then to have presented his story as undisguised biography. He elected to do otherwise, and perhaps he was right ; but by doing so he condemned his book to a period of obscurity in which its outstanding merits remained unrecognised. I do not mean by this that it was a financial failure, for I dare say it sold pretty well as a *succès de scandale* ; but that is not the same thing as earning the critical respect that it deserved.

That Roberts himself knew the book was good is clearly enough demonstrated by the great pains he took to improve it when, in 1923, a new and revised edition was brought out by Nash & Grayson. This 1923 text (which has been used for this edition) is free from many crudities and roughnesses of style that had arisen from the speed with which the original was produced, though in other respects Roberts was too sensible to meddle with his work. There are a few minor differences of fact, one or two of the most important of which are referred to in the footnotes. Otherwise the only way in which the revised text differs from the earlier one is in the suppression of some passages in which Roberts dilates upon himself instead of upon his subject, and a rather marked tendency to be less civil to Wells, with whom, in the interim, his relations had apparently deteriorated.

One difference between the texts is, however, distinctly revealing. The name of W. H. Hudson, at the beginning of chapter XII, is given in the first edition under the pseudonym, Rawson. But Hudson had died in 1922, and the substitution of his actual name for the pseudonym is, I think, a clear indication of the way in which the author's mind was working. Already in the earlier version, the names of such persons as Grant Allen and Cotter Morison, who were dead at the time of writing, had been given without disguise, and it therefore seems obvious that Roberts only used pseudonyms when he felt he could not help it. Their employment, as he could not fail to see, greatly detracted from the authenticity of his book, and it has consequently now seemed more in keeping with the author's own intention to abandon them, particularly as all the actors in his story are dead. In order to make this change, however, two alternatives were open to an editor : he could either alter the names directly in the text, or he could elucidate them in a series of footnotes ; and working on the theory that the final text of an author is, or should be, sacrosanct, it has been thought better to adopt the latter course. Consequently, explanatory footnotes have been appended to the first mention of each pseudonymous character or book title, and in addition, to save the constant irritation of having to turn back the pages, a short index of the principal recurring pseudonyms has been provided at the end of the volume. It is not claimed that all the pseudonyms have been resolved, for some of them do not matter ; but all the main ones have been. Further, such of the footnotes as are marked (R.) are those which Morley Roberts himself supplied to the 1923 edition ; the others are the editor's responsibility.

This business of editing and elucidating the text has necessarily resulted in the present editor forming a pretty strong
opinion on a matter that has been much debated : to what
extent did Morley Roberts, within his fictional framework, tell
the truth ?  H. G. Wells, in the admirable pages of his *Experiment in Autobiography* which deal with Gissing, speaks of *Maitland*
as telling his story " with considerable inaccuracy " ;  and
Dr. Mabel Collins Donnelly in her *George Gissing : Grave
Comedian* (Harvard University Press, 1954) repeats the charge
and says that Roberts was " grievously in error on many
details," though at the same time she concedes that he was
" closely in touch with the main events in his friend's life."
I have therefore been at special pains to check Roberts's state-
ments wherever possible against the information provided in
these two books, also in a third, the curiously bowdlerised
*Letters of George Gissing to His Family*, which first appeared in
1927 ; and where I have come upon a confusion or a contradiction in a matter of fact I have referred to it in a footnote.
I think that these references, in their relative triviality, are the
best evidence that can be advanced to show that Roberts,
when he erred, did so through carelessness or failure of memory
rather than through deliberate intention.  Indeed, having
regard to his declared purpose in writing the book (see his
Preface to the first edition),[1] anything else would have been
the merest self-stultification.  I believe then that, in intention
if not always in practice, he could in all sincerity have appended
to his title page that epigraph from Shakespeare which Balzac
attached to *Père Goriot* : " All is true."  It is for this reason
that I have made the most of his occasional slips, for I
think he would have been glad to have them noticed and
rectified.

All this, needless to say, refers only to matters of fact.  As
regards matters of opinion, Morley Roberts, as I shall try to
show a little later on, was a man of strong character who had
decided views of his own.  He expressed these with the utmost
vigour, and though I have no doubt as to their entire honesty,
I think they were sometimes mistaken.  One case where it
seems to me that he was mistaken is his insistence that Gissing
was really a scholar, and only a novelist by pure force of
circumstance.  I think I know where he got that idea ; he

[1] Appendix A, p. 245.

got it from what Gissing himself says of Reardon, the novelist in *New Grub Street* ; but I think he overdoes it, because it seems perfectly clear that no man who wrote as many novels as Gissing, and who took such obvious pains with them, can have been as totally devoid as Roberts represents him of the true aspirations of the novelist. Besides, even in that same book, Gissing himself gives this theory the lie when he makes Reardon say : " Of course it is not only for the sake of reputation that one tries to do uncommon work. There's the shrinking from conscious insincerity of workmanship. . . . There is no such thing as goodness or badness, in the absolute sense, of course. Perhaps I am absurdly inconsistent when—though knowing my work can't be first rate—I strive to make it as good as possible." Such words as these, in their pride and their humility, are not the words of a man who holds the craft of fiction in disesteem.

A still more striking instance of Roberts's vehement opinions leading him astray is to be found in the almost ludicrous fury with which he fell upon the Anglican chaplain at St. Jean-de-Luz, who had ventured to report that Gissing had died in " the comfort and strength of the Catholic faith ". The chaplain was certainly mistaken, and it was right that his mistake should have been corrected ; yet it is also clear that his mistake was an honest one. Wells's account of the matter in his *Experiment in Autobiography* here provides a valuable corrective to Roberts's narration. In his description of Gissing's last hours, Wells relates how in his delirium he " babbled in Latin and chanted fragments of Gregorian music ", for his mind was running on the material he had accumulated for his last novel, the historical romance, *Veranilda*.

> The Anglican chaplain [Wells continues] . . . heard of that chanting. He allowed his impression to develop in his memory and it was proclaimed later in a newspaper that Gissing had died in the fear of God's holy name, and with the comfort and strength of the Catholic faith. This led to some bitter recriminations. Edward Clodd and Morley Roberts were particularly enraged at this " body-snatching," as they called it, and among other verbal missiles that hit that kindly little man in the full publicity of print were " crow," " vulture," and " ecclesiastical buzzard." But he did not deserve to be called such names. He did quite honestly think Gissing's " *Te Deums* " had some sort of spiritual significance.

In fairness to Roberts, though, it should be added that, as he did not arrive at St. Jean-Pied-de-Port until after Gissing's death, he did not have the same opportunity as Wells for knowing the cause of the chaplain's mistake.

It is interesting, and perhaps at this point not entirely irrelevant, to note that, in an accomplished essay in *The New Statesman* of February 7, 1953, Walter Allen has pointed out how Gissing's deathbed delirium was stored up in the mind of Wells to emerge later during the last hours of a very different kind of character—Uncle Ponderevo in *Tono-Bungay*. " What are these magnificent beings ? " Wells represents Gissing as saying. " Who are these magnificent beings advancing upon us ? What is all this splendour ? What does it portend ? " And Uncle Ponderevo, in the same vein, in an obscure French inn, under the eyes of yet another little Anglican parson, is made to cry aloud : " What is this great place, these cloud-capped towers, these airy pinnacles ? . . . Ilion. Sky-y-pointing. . . . Terrace above terrace. . . . Reaching to the Heavens. . . . Kingdoms Cæsar never knew," and so on. What is perhaps even more curious is that this portentous vision of an older world was not the first which Gissing had experienced. When in 1897 he lay ill at Cotrone, as he tells us in *By the Ionian Sea*, he fell into

> A visionary state which, whilst it lasted, gave me such placid happiness as I have never known when in my perfect mind. Lying still and calm, and perfectly awake, I watched a succession of wonderful pictures. First of all I saw great vases, rich with ornament and figures ; then sepulchral marbles, carved more exquisitely than the most beautiful I had ever known. The vision grew in extent, in multiplicity of detail ; presently I was regarding scenes of ancient life—thronged streets, processions triumphal or religious, halls of feasting, fields of battle. What most impressed me at the time was the marvellously bright yet delicate colouring of everything I saw. I can give no idea in words of the pure radiance which shone from every object, which illumined every scene.

And again, and more remarkable still, is the fact that, as early as 1890 when he was writing of the last illness of Reardon in *New Grub Street*, he had bestowed upon his dying hero similar dreams :

> He was at Patras, was stepping into a boat to be rowed out to the steamer which would bear him away from Greece. A magnificent night, though at the end of December ; a sky

of deep blue, thick set with stars. . . . The water was as deep
a blue as the sky, and sparkled with reflected radiance.

And now he stood on deck in the light of early morning.
Southward lay the Ionian Islands; he looked for Ithaca, and
grieved that it had been passed in the hours of darkness. But
the nearest point of the main shore was a rocky promontory ;
it reminded him that in these waters was fought the battle of
Actium.

There is strange fitness in the fact that Gissing's last hours
should have been irradiated with a vision not unlike that
which he had given to Reardon ; and that both of these
visions were of the ancient world is, I suggest, proof sufficient
that Wells's failure to understand this side of Gissing's personality is the chief blemish in the portrait which he has given
us of him. I mention the matter here because his account is
the only one at all worthy to stand beside that of Morley
Roberts, and it is largely because of its blank and total in-
comprehension of Gissing's classicism that it falls short. The
passage in which Wells ventilates his views is so characteristic
and so interesting that I venture to give it here :

> The insanity of our educational organisation [he wrote] had
> planted down in that Yorkshire town, a . . . school dominated
> by the idea of classical scholarship. The head was an enthusi-
> astic pedant who poured into that fresh and vigorous young
> brain nothing but classics and a " scorn " for non-classical
> things. Gissing's imagination, therefore, escaped from the
> cramping gentilities and respectabilities of home to find its
> compensations in the rhetorical swagger, the rotundities and
> the pompous grossness of Rome. He walked about Wakefield
> in love with goddesses and nymphs and excited by ideas of
> patrician freedom in a world of untouchable women. . . . He
> accepted and identified himself with all the pretensions of
> Rome's triumphal arches.

Morley Roberts, who himself had had a classical education,
wrote in a different strain, and I do not think there is much
doubt who gives the truer picture.

To this conception of *Maitland* as picture, I now for a
moment return. It explains much, the heightening by simpli-
fication of detail, the absence of dates. Roberts had friends
who were painters, and as he himself says : " There is great
advantage in describing things as they impress themselves on
the writer. A portrait gains in coherency and completeness
by temporary omissions more than it can ever gain by the

empty endeavour to handle each period fully." If we look at *Henry Maitland* in that light, as an impression of one man seen through the eyes of another who knew him well, and who knew him too at a time when no one else in any degree articulate knew him, I think we may best gauge its value. On the point of detail, Dr. Donnelly, I see, makes great play with the fact that she thinks she has discovered that Gissing met his second wife in " a coffee-shop on Oxford Street " (which she somehow seems to imagine makes it all much more respectable), whereas Wells says he " picked her up " one Sunday in Regent's Park, and Roberts boldly declares that he " rushed out " and spoke to the first woman he came across in the Marylebone Road. This, to the mind of Dr. Donnelly, appears a grave inaccuracy ; but the fact is, of course, that Roberts is not only giving the true impression of the thing as he saw it at the time, but also the impression of the thing as it actually and essentially was. The absence of dates, on the other hand, may perhaps deprive the book of some of its feeling of authenticity, and so I have supplied in the footnotes those which seem most relevant. It was, of course, impossible for Roberts, working within his special terms of reference, to do this, even if he had wanted to.

One word more, this time a personal one, and I have finished with Gissing's side of the story. In 1950 I was myself at St. Jean-de-Luz and there visited his grave high up at the very top of the cemetery which commands a noble prospect over the Bay of Biscay. Close beside him is the grave of another English writer, E. W. Hornung, the creator of *Raffles* ; and not far off is that of Edmund Candler, who wrote *The Unveiling of Lhasa*. It seemed a strange little symposium of talented men ; and as I tidied up Gissing's rather neglected tomb, I could not help thinking there was an irony in this random juxtaposition of literary characters who had never met in life, such as he would have appreciated.

(2)

Much has been written and will continue to be written of George Gissing, for though his place in English letters has not been finally determined, the piecemeal but continuous reprinting of his books indicates that there is lively interest in his work. The case is otherwise, I am afraid, at present, with

Morley Roberts, though I think that anyone who reads his *Henry Maitland* will wonder why. Some of the best books in the world are in essence a collaboration between two men ; between the writer and his subject, between the active and the sleeping partner in the enterprise. Boswell's *Johnson* is such a book, and so are Hazlitt's *Conversations of Northcote* and Dyce's *Table Talk of Samuel Rogers* ; and it may be that posterity will some day reckon *Maitland* of this company. Yet it has taken more than a century for the idea to sink in that Boswell was as great a man as his subject, and Dyce is still regarded as little better than an editor. The fact seems to be, indeed, that there are some books so interesting in their subject-matter that the reader tends to believe they have written themselves.

This is an error. A book such as *Henry Maitland* does not write itself, but is, on the contrary, the deliberately planned work of a skilful and intelligent artist. It is only fitting, therefore—since it happens to be his centenary too—that we should here take a closer look at Morley Charles Roberts and see what we can discover concerning him.

He was born in London in, as we have noted earlier, the December of 1857, the son of an inspector of Income Tax ; and after having begun his education at Bedford Grammar School he completed it at Owens College, Manchester, where he first met Gissing. When he was nineteen he quarrelled bitterly with his father and went off to Australia ; and there, during the years 1876 to 1878, he roughed it, working on the Victorian railroads and on the sheep and cattle runs of the New South Wales bush. He next became an able-bodied seaman, sailing before the mast in the *Essex*, the *Corona*, and other vessels, ultimately thus making his way back to England in " a Blackwell barque". He came home in 1879.

These primitive experiences had not, however, destroyed his love of letters ; and when in 1880 he again met Gissing, though he was ostensibly clerking at tenpence an hour in the War Office and, later, the India Office, his real life was in his reading and in the literary plans he was revolving. But the routine of a civil servant's life was more than he could endure for long, and besides, a strain of something that seems nearly to resemble hypochondria was already becoming apparent in him. His health was, or appeared to him to be, in a bad

way ; and in 1884 he set forth again on his travels, going first
this time to Texas, where he joined his brother, Cecil, and
thence proceeding by slow and laborious stages through Iowa
and Minnesota to the Canadian Rockies and British Columbia,
he reached San Francisco at last in the winter of 1885–86.
This is a journey fully documented for us, since it forms the
subject of his first and in some respects his best-known book,
*The Western Avernus.*

This, which first appeared in 1887, was later honoured by
inclusion in Everyman's Library, to which it was added in
1924. It is, in addition to being an astonishingly vivid picture
of life in the States and Canada during the semi-roaring
'eighties, a valuable record (and almost the only one available
to us for this period) of the very singular man who had written
it. Roberts in those days was a tall, restless, brown-haired,
brown-eyed, red-bearded, powerful yet neurotic man, already
a confirmed pessimist and rationalist, whose aesthetic sensibili-
ties were nevertheless abnormally developed. His special form
of pessimism, as he tells us, was one which permitted him only
to see beauty in art—in the pictures of Turner, the music of
Beethoven, the poetry of the moderns—by which he meant
such poets as Tennyson, Rossetti, and Blake. He carried
*Sartor Resartus* with him in his pocket, and later on, Virgil,
and he was often in ecstacies over the natural beauties which
everywhere surrounded him ; but for all that he worked hard
at any heavy job that was going, on railroad construction
(including a spell on the then uncompleted Canadian Pacific
Railway), in saw-mills, and on farms, and he was not infrequently down to his last cent. The final pages of the book
describe his nightmare experiences when he is completely
down-and-out in San Francisco, and they make sombre reading. Nevertheless his vitality was prodigious : he traversed vast
distances on foot, he involved himself with the toughest kinds
of travelling-companions, and he learnt a good deal of the hobo
art of living on nothing a week, upon which, years later, another
British man of letters, W. H. Davies, was to expatiate so admirably in his *Autobiography of a Super-Tramp.* Yet for all Roberts's
vitality, it was not quite of the normal kind : despite everything he maintained his basic sensitivity, and indeed if his
book is to be faulted at all it is for the not infrequent passages
in it where this sensitivity comes out as immoderate pugnacity,

H.M.—2

or as simple self-pity. After all, one can hardly help feeling sometimes as one reads him that he had asked for it. He may have descended into Avernus, but it was a voluntary descent, and one, moreover, very different from that which is made by those who have no alternative, nor any certain hope of return. Yet, save for this slightly factitious quality, *The Western Avernus* remains a fine record of travel and hardship, and in addition it has the great merit that it defines for us, right from the start, the four strands in Roberts's temperament that give him, and his work, their special quality. These were, his exuberant physical vitality ; his robust but very real sense of humour ; his profoundly pessimistic rationalism ; and his suppressed but always underlying neurotic sensibility. It was an uncommon, though not unique, combination ; and I think it may be traced through all he was later to do.

In 1887 he was back in London and at once set to work on his book, in circumstances much as they are described in *Henry Maitland*. His life thereafter, though for the first fifteen or sixteen years nothing like success came to him, was one of almost unceasing literary toil, which he diversified by occasional bursts of travel that carried him to Africa, the South Seas, and indeed, eventually, almost all over the globe. For the next half-century, books of every kind came from his pen— poems, stories, novels, plays, travel books, political, social, and biological studies ; and when he died on June 8, 1942, in his eighty-fifth year, his publications amounted to well over seventy. In his prime he had often produced three books a year, and for a much longer period never less than two. It is only natural that, with such fertility, some of his work should now be forgotten, and indeed a good deal of it is virtually impossible to find. Even so, in addition to *Maitland* and *The Western Avernus*, it is necessary to say a word at least upon the two diametrically opposed aspects of his talent that were responsible, on the one hand, for his longest, and I suppose his longest-lived, novel, *Rachel Marr* (1903) and, on the other, for his splendid sea stories, the cream of which appeared in 1913 under the title of *Salt of the Sea*.

It is always difficult, I suppose, for critical opinion to think itself back into the intellectual climate of the day before yesterday, and yet unless we can do just this it is very nearly impossible to understand why Roberts's friend, W. H. Hudson, was able uncompromisingly to declare *Rachel Marr* " a great novel ". To us to-day the book seems, on the contrary, hardly more than an ambitious exercise in all those things for which Roberts's equipment least fitted him. It is a tragic love story in the largest Elizabethan manner, though the setting is modern ; and it is principally composed in semi-Biblical prose. Had it come off it would have won itself a place by the side of *Wuthering Heights,* but to a present-day taste it does not come off, and this is a great pity, for there is no doubt that Roberts put into it all that he had, in this particular vein.

Yet one of the most curious things about the writers of the first decade of the present century is that they seem often to have been totally unaware of their true range. E. Nesbit was a case in point, for she valued highly her pretentious poems and novels, and thought little of the children's stories which now constitute her real claim to immortality. In the same way it would appear that Roberts himself thought far more of such work as he had put into *Rachel Marr* than he did of the magnificent sea stories to which I have referred. Yet there can be no doubt now that it was here that his best gifts were displayed. These stories have a racy humour, an ingenuity, an unflagging invention which seem to me to put them into a class equal or superior to the best work of that neglected (or perhaps he is no longer neglected) genius, W. W. Jacobs. Anyone who cannot derive great recreation and refreshment from such tales as *The Captain of the Ullswater, The Rehabilitation of the Vigia*, or that little masterpiece of the terrible, *Jack-all-alone*, has my sympathy ; and I would couple with these that delicious story from another collection, *The Tale of Brazos Dick*. It is not merely Roberts's faculty for brilliant improvisation and his easy command of narrative and speech-rhythms that make these stories memorable, it is the fact that they have authority, that you perceive them to be the work of a man who knows his subject inside out. Even Jacobs's mariners are mere coast-hugging comedians by the side of Roberts's deep-water seamen.

It is perhaps not impossible to give some sort of mental picture of this man who, even as early as 1912, Swinnerton had noted as " obviously liable to painful excitements, even nervous breakdown ", and whom he depicts during their first, and I think their only, meeting as " quivering with agitation " over the adverse reviews of *Maitland*. Yet perhaps Roberts's quiverings were understandable, for had he not written of the book : " If it is not a defence—what can I say ? " and he was a man whose sense of loyalty to his friends was very great. His mistake, in this case, had been to believe that the truth was the best defence ; that to know all was to forgive all ; and he had been bitterly disillusioned. Nevertheless he continued to serve what he conceived to be his friend's interests, and during the 'twenties he prevailed upon his then publishers, Nash & Grayson, to reissue a number of Gissing's novels, to each of which he contributed a critical foreword. And when the other friend who really mattered to him—Hudson—died in 1922, it was he again who was called in, almost as a matter of course, to reshape the only partially legible fragments which constituted the final chapter of his last book, *A Hind in Richmond Park* ; and later still, in 1924, he wrote Hudson's first biography, which was described, significantly enough in the present connection, as " A Portrait." It was not by accident that when, in 1924, he came to reissue *The Western Avernus*, the names which stood upon the dedication page were those of his dead friends—George Gissing and W. H. Hudson.

Many years before, as Roberts himself tells in *Maitland*, Gissing had portrayed him in various of his novels. " Some of the sketches," as he observes, " are fairly complimentary, and many are much the reverse." I think I know in which category he would have included the exuberant figure of Malkin, in *Born in Exile* :

> A tall man, in a light overcoat and a straw hat of spacious brim, had seized both his hands, with shouts of excited greeting. " Confound you ! Why did you keep me waiting ? I thought I had missed you for the evening. How the deuce are you ? And why the devil have you left me without a line from you for more than six months ? "
>
> Earwaker drew aside, and allowed his tumultuous friend to rush into the nearest room.
>
> " Why haven't you written ?—confound you ! " was again vociferated, amid bursts of boyish laughter. " Why hasn't anybody written ? "
>
> " If everybody was as well informed of your movements as I, I don't wonder," replied the journalist. " Since you left Buenos Ayres, I have had two letters, each containing twenty words, which gave me to understand that no answer could by possibility reach you."
>
> " Humbug ! You could have written to half a dozen likely places. Did I really say that ? Ha, ha, ha ! Shake hands

again, confound you ! How do you do ? Do I look well ?
Have I a tropical colour ? . . . What a time I've had ! What
a time I've had ! "

And Gissing goes on to say that it was more than twelve months
since Malkin had left England :

> Though sun and sea had doubtless contributed to his robust-
> ness, he must always have been a fair example of the vigorous
> Briton. His broad shoulders, upright bearing, open counten-
> ance, and frank resonant voice, declared a youth passed amid
> the wholesome conditions which wealth alone can command.
> [A fine unsolicited tribute, incidentally, to the then status of
> Inland Revenue officials.] The hearty extravagance of his
> friendliness was only possible in a man who has never been
> humiliated by circumstances, never restricted in his natural
> needs of body and mind. Yet he had more than the hearti-
> ness of a contented Englishman. The vivacity which made a
> whirlwind about him probably indicated some ancestral
> mingling with the blood of a more ardent race.

It is not in Gissing's best manner, though the last two
sentences are uncommonly revealing. And then, later on in
the same novel—and it is immensely curious to note that these
pages must have been written just after Roberts's attempt to
prevent Gissing's second marriage—Malkin is himself represented as involved in frightful pre-matrimonial complications.
The point is one of some subtlety, for it seems clear that Gissing,
whether consciously or otherwise, is revenging himself upon
Roberts for his well-intended intervention. Malkin's trouble
is that, while intending to pay court to the young daughter
of a widow, he finds himself suddenly proposing to the widow
instead :

> " Oh, ass that I was ! " [he cries].
> He smote the side of his head savagely.
> " Can you guess, Earwaker ? Can you give a shot at what
> happened ? "
> " Perhaps I might," replied the other, gravely.
> " Well ? "
> " That woman asked you to marry her."
> Malkin leapt from his chair, and sank back again.
> " It came to that. Yes, upon my word, it came to that.
> She said she had fallen in love with me. . . . Oh, confound it !
> What a frightful scene it was ! "
> " You took a final leave of her ? "
> Malkin stared with eyes of anguish into his friend's face,
> and at length whispered thickly :
> " I said I would ! "

" What ?   Take leave ? "

" Marry her ! "

Earwaker had much ado to check an impatiently remon-
strant laugh.  He paused awhile, then began his expostulation,
at first treating the affair as too absurd for grave argument.

" My boy," he concluded, " you have got into a preposterous
scrape, and I see only one way out of it.   You must flee.
When does your brother start for the Antipodes ? "

" I can't bring myself to that," came in a groan from
Malkin.   " I've never yet done anything to be seriously
ashamed of, and I can't run away after promising marriage.
It would weigh upon me for the rest of my life."

Assuredly, though the voice here is the voice of Gissing, the
hand is the hand of Roberts.  The transposing of the roles,
so long now after the event, has a devastating irony to those
who know the story.

It would, however, take much too long to touch upon all
the portraits of Roberts that are to be found in Gissing's pages.
Whelpdale, in *New Grub Street*, is, as Swinnerton has noted, a
rough sketch for Malkin, with his romantic propensities still
more in evidence ; and there is yet another version of him in
*The Emancipated*.  It was inevitable that Gissing should draw
from him largely, for his personal acquaintance at the time
was desperately restricted.

To turn from these early and irreverent portrayals of this
turbulent and lively man to a contemplation of Roberts's later
years is a saddening business, for these later years, on the
whole, were obscure.  He continued with great regularity to
publish books, though I doubt whether they received much
attention after 1914, when his *Time and Thomas Waring*—a
remarkable account of his experiences under an anæsthetic—
enjoyed a considerable and deserved success.  But in 1928 he
lectured at the Royal Institution on *The Sea in Fiction*, and one
year later gave further proof of his versatility by exhibiting at
the Abbey Gallery a collection of his water-colours of Jamaica.
In his last book but one, *Bio-Politics* (1938), he returned to the
biological considerations which he had first outlined in the
best of his scientific books, *Malignancy and Evolution* (1926).
His doctrine, to put it much too simply, was the cheerless
though not necessarily erroneous one, that the law of the jungle
and the immutable principles of international conduct are
exactly the same thing.  The events which followed close on
the heels of this publication did not do much to refute his view.

One of those who knew him best in his later years was Margaret Storm Jameson, who has very kindly sent me this perceptive and moving account of him :

> I knew Morley Roberts only during the last few years of his life, shortly before his step-daughter, with whom he lived, died. He compelled respect and affection. His mind was what it had always been, a cutting instrument. He held firmly to his agnostic and materialistic beliefs. His courage—physical and moral—was as clear in him as his intelligence. He was not happy in the years I knew him ; he felt that he had outlived his time and almost all his friends, and that he was unduly neglected as a writer. Which is true. There was something impersonal about his bitterness—it was as if he were bitter on behalf of all his fellow-generation of giants.

That last touch is surely typical ; for Roberts, beyond all else, was a true man of letters, and it was natural that it should be less the neglect of himself than that of his generation and all it had stood for, that deepest wounded him.

Storm Jameson continues :

> The books he rated highest when I knew him were his scientific books, notably *Malignancy and Evolution*. . . .
> He was very tall, very thin without being slight, because he had broad shoulders, a *strong* delicate face, if that isn't too contradictory. Very elegant in his shabby way—he often wore a dressing-gown when you called on him during the daytime. He was painting a lot—not good pictures, but curiously interesting in a spectral way.
> He suffered terribly when his step-daughter died. After that he was really alone.
> Much of his life is told by himself in his travel books. He talked very little of his personal life to me, so that I knew nothing about his marriage, for example.

Nor can I do much to supply this information, except to add that, in 1896, he married Alice Selous, who I believe was a connection, possibly a cousin, of the celebrated Victorian big-game hunter of that name ; and that the first (1912), but not the revised, edition of *Henry Maitland* is dedicated " To the Memory of My Wife."

At his death, Morley Roberts left Storm Jameson some or all of his papers and books, and the latter—his presentation-copies of Gissing and Hudson, as well as his copies of his own works—were given by her to Leeds University, where they now form a small Morley Roberts Library of some two hundred volumes. One cannot but hope that some day, with the aid of this collection and of his papers, someone will undertake a fuller and more adequate memorial of this turbulent, talented, and lovable man of letters after the vanished mode, than I have been able to furnish here.

M. B.

# THE PRIVATE LIFE OF
# HENRY MAITLAND

# I

IT is never an easy thing to write the life, or even such a sketch as I propose to make, of a friend whom one knew well, and in Henry Maitland's [1] case it is uncommonly difficult. The usual biographer is content with writing panegyric, and as he must depend for his material, and even sometimes for his eventual remuneration, on the relatives of his subject, he is from the start in a hopeless position, except, it may be, as regards the public side of the life in question. But in the case of a man of letters the personal element is the only real and valuable one, or so it seems to me, and even if I were totally ignorant of Maitland's work I think it would yet be possible for me to do a lifelike sketch of him. I believe, moreover, that it is my duty to do it, although it may be painful to those connected with him. Yet soon after his death many came and asked me to write his biography. It was an understood thing that of all his friends I knew him best, and was certainly the chief authority on his career from the Moorhampton College [2] days up to his final break with his second wife. But in 1904 there were many obstacles to my doing this work. His two sons were young. His sisters and his mother were still alive. I say nothing of the wife herself, then being taken care of, or of a third lady of whom I must speak presently. Several people came to me with proposals about a book on Henry Maitland. One of the partners of a big publishing house made me a definite offer for it on behalf of his firm. On the other hand one of his executors, Miss

---

[1] George Gissing (1857–1903)  [2] Owens College, Manchester.

Kingdon,[1] a most kindly and amiable and very able woman employed in a great accountant's office in the city, who had done very much for Henry Maitland in his later life, begged me not to do the book, or if I did it to hold it over until her responsibilities as executrix and trustee for the sons were at an end. But it is now nearly nine years since he died, and I feel that if I do not put down at once what I knew of him it never will be written, and something will be lost, something which has perhaps a little value, even though not so great as those could wish who knew and loved Henry Maitland.

There is no doubt that many people will accuse me of desiring to use his memory for my own advantage. " My withers are unwrung." Those who speak in this way must have little knowledge of the poor profit to be derived from writing such a book, and the proportion of that profit to the labour employed in it. On three separate occasions I spoke to Maitland about writing his biography, and it was an understood thing between us that if he died before me I was to write his life and tell the whole and absolute truth about him. This he gave me the most definite permission to do. I believe he felt that it might in some ways be of service to humanity for such a book to be written. Only the other day, when I wrote to Miss Kingdon concerning the biography, she answered me : " If I seem lacking in cordiality in this matter do not attribute it to any want of sympathy with you. I am not attempting to dissuade you. Henry Maitland was sent into hell for the purpose of saving souls ; perhaps it is a necessary thing that his story should be written by all sorts of people from their different points of view." Once I proposed to him to use his character and career as the chief figure in a long story. He wrote to me, " By all

[1] Clara Collet (1860–1948) : she was in fact a Civil Servant.

means.  Why not ? "  Had I not the letter in which he said this I should myself almost doubt my own recollection, but it is certain that he knew the value of his own experience, and felt that he might perhaps by his example save some from suffering as he suffered.

No doubt very much that I say of him will not be true to others.  To myself at any rate it is true.  We know very little of each other, and after all it is perhaps in biography that one is most acutely conscious of the truth in the pragmatic view of truth.  Those things are true in Henry Maitland's life and character which fit in wholly with all my experience of him and make a coherent and likely theory.  I used to think I knew him very well, and yet when I remember and reflect it seems to me that I know exceedingly little about him.  And yet again, I am certain that of the two people in the world with whom I was best acquainted he was one.  We go through life believing that we know many, but if we sit down and attempt to draw them we find here and there unrelated facts and many vague incoherencies.  We are in a fog about our very dear friend whom but yesterday we were ready to judge and criticise with an air of final knowledge.  There is something humiliating in this, and yet how should we, who know so little of ourselves, know even those we love ?  To my mind, with all his weaknesses, which I shall not extenuate, Maitland was a noble and notable character, and if anything I should write may endure but a little while it is because there is really something of him in my words.  I am far more concerned to write about Henry Maitland for those who loved him than for those who loved him not, and I shall be much better pleased if what I do about him takes the shape of an impression rather than of anything like an ordinary biography.  Every important and unimportant political fool who dies nowadays is buried under obituary notices and a mausoleum in two volumes—a mausoleum which is, as a rule, about as high a work of art as the angels on tombstones in an early Victorian cemetery. But Maitland, I think, deserves, if not a better, a more sympathetic tribute.

When I left Radford [1] Grammar School my father, being in the Civil Service, was sent to Moorhampton [2] as Surveyor of Taxes, and his family soon followed him. I continued my own education at Moorhampton College, which was then beginning to earn a high reputation as an educational centre. Some months before I met Maitland personally I knew his reputation was that of an extraordinary young scholar. Even as a boy of sixteen he swept everything before him. There was nobody in the place who could touch him at classical learning, and everybody prophesied the very greatest future for the boy. I met him first in a little hotel, not very far from the College, where some of us young fellows used to go in the intervals of lectures to play a game of billiards. I remember quite well seeing him sit on a little table swinging his legs, and to this day I can remember somewhat of the impression he made upon me. He was curiously bright, with a very mobile face. He had abundant masses of brown hair combed backwards over his head, grey-blue eyes, a very sympathetic mouth, an extraordinarily well-shaped chin —although perhaps both mouth and chin were a little weak—and a great capacity for talking and laughing.

Henceforth he and I became very firm friends at the College, although we belonged to two entirely different sets. I was supposed to be an extraordinarily rowdy person, and was always getting into trouble both with the authorities and with my fellows, and he was a man

---

[1] Bedford.    [2] Manchester.

who loathed anything like rowdiness, could not fight if he tried, objected even then to the Empire, hated patriotism, and thought about nothing but ancient Greece and Rome, or so it would appear to those who knew him at that time.

I learnt then a little of his early history. Even when he was but a boy of ten or eleven he was recognised as a creature of most brilliant promise. He always believed that he owed most, and perhaps everything, to his father,[1] who must have been a very remarkable man. Henry never spoke about him in later life without emotion and affection. I have often thought since that Maitland felt that most of his disasters sprang from the premature death of his father, whom he loved so tenderly. Indeed the elder man must have been a remarkable figure, a gentle, courtly, and most kindly man, himself born in exile and placed in alien circumstances. Maitland often used to speak, with a catch in his voice, of the way his father read to him. I do not remember what books he read, but they were the classic authors of England ; Shakespeare, Wordsworth, and Tennyson. Some seem to imagine that the father had what is called a well-stocked library. This was not true, but he had many good books and taught his son to love them. Among these there was one great volume of Hogarth's drawings which came into Henry Maitland's personal possession, only, I think, when he was finally domiciled in a London flat, where he and I often looked at it. It is curious that even as a boy Hogarth had a fascination for him. He sometimes copied these drawings, for as a child he had no little skill as a draughtsman. What appealed to him in later days in Hogarth was the power of the man's satire, his painful bitterness, which can be equalled only by the ironies of Swift in another

[1] Thomas Waller Gissing (1829–70).

medium. Although personally I admire Hogarth I
could never look at him with anything like pleasure or,
indeed, without acute discomfort. I remember that
Maitland in later years said in his book about the
Victorian Novelists [1] : " With these faces who would
spend hours of leisure ? Hogarth copied in the strict
sense of the word. He gives us life and we cannot
bear it."

Maitland's family came, I think, from Worcester,
but something led the elder Maitland to Mirefields [2]
and there he came in contact with a chemist called
Lake,[3] whose business he presently bought. Perhaps
the elder Maitland was not a wholly happy man. He
was very gentle, but not a person of marked religious
feeling. Indeed I think the attitude of the family at
that time was one of free thought. From everything
that Henry said of his father it always seemed to me
that the man had been an alien in the cold Yorkshire
town where his son was born. And Maitland knew that
had his father lived he would never have been thrown
alone into the great city of Moorhampton, " Lord of
himself, that heritage of woe." Not all women comprehend the dangers that their sons may meet in such
surroundings, and those who had charge of Henry
Maitland's future never understood or recognised them
in his youth. But his father would have known. In
one chapter of the " The Vortex," [4] there is very much
of Maitland. It is a curiously wrought picture of a
father and his son in which he himself played alternately
the part of father and child. I knew his anxieties for
his own children, and on reading that chapter one sees
them renewed. But in it there was much that was not
himself. It was drawn rather from what he believed

[1] *Charles Dickens : a Critical Study* (1898).   [2] Wakefield.
[3] Hick (see p. 26 for Dr. Henry Hick, his son).
[4] *The Whirlpool* (1897).

his father had felt. In " The Vortex " the little boy
spends an hour alone with his father just before bedtime,
and he calls it " A golden hour, sacred to memories of
the world's own childhood."

Maitland went to school in Mirefields and this school
has been called a kind of " Dotheboys Hall," which of
course is absolutely ridiculous. It was not, in fact, a
boarding-school at all, but a day school. The man
who ran it was called Hinkson.[1] Maitland said he
was an uneducated man, or at any rate uneducated
from his point of view in later years, yet he was a person
of very remarkable character, and, taking it all round,
did very good work. A man named Christopher
started this school and sold it to Hinkson, who had, I
believe, some kind of a degree obtained at Durham.
The boys who attended it were good middle class and
lower middle class, some the sons of professional men,
some the offspring of the richer tradesmen. Upon the
whole it was a remarkably good school for that time.
Many of the boys actually left the Grammar School at
Mirefields to attend it. Henry Maitland always owned
that Hinkson took great pains with his scholars, and
affirmed that many owed him much. As I said, the
general religious air of Maitland's home at that time
was not orthodox. I believe the feminine members of
the family attended a Unitarian Church, but the father
did not go to church at all. One example of this
religious attitude of his home came out when Hinkson
called on his boys to repeat the collect of the day and
Maitland replied abruptly that they did not do that
kind of thing at home. Whereupon Hinkson promptly
set him to learn it, saying sternly that it would do him
no harm.

For the most part in those early days the elder

[1] Harrison.

Maitland and his son spent Sunday afternoon in the garden belonging to their Mirefields house. Oddly enough this garden was not attached to the dwelling but was a kind of allotment. It has been photographically reproduced by Henry Maitland in the seventh chapter of the first volume of " Morning." [1] Very often Henry Maitland's father read to him in that garden.

One of Maitland's schoolfellows at Hinkson's school was the son of the man from whom his father had bought the druggist's business. The elder Lake was a friend of Barry Sullivan, and theatrically mad. He started plays in which Henry always took some part, though not the prominent part which has been attributed to him by some people. Nevertheless he was always interested in plays and had a very dramatic way of reading anything that was capable of dramatic interpretation. He always loved the sound of words, and even when first at Moorhampton he took down a German book and read some of it aloud to the younger Lake,[2] who did not know German and said so. Whereupon Maitland shook his fist at him and said : " But Lake, listen, listen, listen—doesn't it *sound* fine ? " This endured through all his life. At school he used to read Oliver Wendell Holmes aloud to some of the other boys. This was when he was thirteen. Even then he always laid stress on beautiful words and loved their rhythm.

His father being a poor man, there would have been little opportunity for Henry Maitland to go to Moorhampton and to its great college if he had not obtained some scholarship. This became even more imperative when his father died. He did obtain this scholarship

[1] *A Life's Morning* (1888).
[2] Henry Hick, later Dr. Hick of New Romney.

when he was somewhere about sixteen, and immediately afterwards was sent over to Moorhampton quite alone and put into lodgings there. At his school in Mirefields he had taken every possible prize, and I think it was two exhibitions from the London University which enabled him to go to Moorhampton. The college was a curious institution, one of the earliest endeavours to create a kind of university centre in a great provincial city. We certainly had a very wonderful staff there, especially on the scientific side. Among the men of science at the college were Sir Henry Bissell [1] ; Schorstein,[2] the great chemist ; Hahn,[3] also a chemist, and Balfour,[4] the physicist. On the classical side were Professor Little [5] and Professor Henry Parker,[6] who were not by any means so notable as their scientific colleagues. The eminence of our scientific professors did not matter very much, perhaps, from Henry Maitland's point of view, for from the day of his birth to the day of his death, he took no interest whatever in science and loathed all forms of speculative thought with a peculiar and almost amusing horror. Mathematics he detested, and if in later years I ever attempted to touch upon metaphysical questions he used to shut up, to use an American phrase, just like a clam. But on the classical side he was much more than merely successful. He took every prize open to him. In his book " The Exile," [7] there is a picture of a youth on prize day going up to receive prize after prize, and I know that this chapter contains much of what he himself must have

[1] Sir Henry Enfield Roscoe, Professor of Chemistry, 1857–86.
[2] Carl Schorlemmer, Professor of Organic Chemistry, 1874–92.
[3] Possibly Dittmar.
[4] Balfour Stewart, Professor of Natural Philosophy, 1870–87.
[5] J. G. Greenwood, Professor of Greek, 1851–85 ; Principal of Owens College, 1857–89.
[6] Augustus S. Wilkins, Professor of Latin, 1869–1903.
[7] Born in Exile (1892).

felt when I saw him retire to a modest back bench loaded with books bound in calf and tooled in gold.

Of course a college of this description, which was not, properly speaking, a university, could only be regarded, for a boy of his culture, as a stepping-stone to one of the older universities, probably Cambridge, since most of my own friends who did go to the university went there from Moorhampton. I do not think there was a professor or lecturer or a single student in the college who did not anticipate for Henry Maitland one of the brightest futures, so far as success at the university could make it so. It is possible that I alone out of those who regarded him with admiration and affection had some doubt of this, and that was not because I disagreed as a boy with any of the estimates that had been formed of him, but simply because for some reason or another he chose me as a confidant. Many years afterwards he said to me with painful bitterness : " It was a cruel and most undesirable thing that I, at the age of sixteen, should have been turned loose in a big city, compelled to live alone in lodgings, with nobody interested in me but those at the college. I see now that one of my sisters should certainly have been sent with me to Moorhampton."

One day he showed me a photograph. It was that of a young girl, aged perhaps seventeen—he at the time being very little more—with her hair down her back. She was not beautiful, but had a certain prettiness, the mere prettiness of youth, and she was undoubtedly not a lady. After some interrogation on my part he told me that she was a young prostitute whom he knew, and it will not be exaggerating my own feelings to say that I recognised instinctively and at once that if his relations with her were not put an end to some kind of disaster was in front of him. It was not that I knew very much about life, for what could a boy of less than eighteen really know about it ?—but I had some kind of instinctive sense in me and was perfectly aware, even then, that Henry Maitland had about as little of it as anybody I had ever met up to that time, or anybody I could ever expect to meet.  It may seem strange to some that even at that time I had no rigid moral views, and extremely little religion, although I thought about it sufficiently to become deliberately a Unitarian, refusing to be confirmed in the English Church, very much to the rage of the parish clergyman, and with the result of much friction with my father.  Yet I had some wisdom and did my best to get Maitland to give up this girl.  He would not do so, and the thing went on, so far as I am aware, for the best part of a year.  He did all he could, apparently, to get Marian Hilton [1] to leave the streets.  He even bought a sewing machine and gave it her with this view.  That was another sample of his early idealism.

This was in 1876, and the younger Lake, who was three years older than Maitland, had then just qualified as a doctor.  He was an assistant at Darwen and one day went over to Moorhampton to see Henry, who told him what he had told me about this Marian Hilton. He even went so far as to say that he was going to marry her.  Dr. Lake, being older, and knowing a little of life through his own profession, did not approve of this and objected strongly.  Afterwards he regretted a thousand times that he had not written direct to Maitland's people to tell them of what was going on.  Yet, although he was the older man, he was not so much older as to have got rid of the boyish loyalty of one youth to another, and he did not do what he knew he ought to have done. It is only fair to say he was still very young.  He found

[1] Marianne Helen Harrison (? 1858–88).

out later that Maitland had even sold his father's watch to help this girl. This affair was also known to a young accountant who came from Mirefields, but with whom I was not acquainted, and also to another man at the college who is now in the Government Service. So far as I remember the accountant was not a good influence, but his other friend did what he could to get Maitland to break off this very undesirable relationship, with no more success than myself.

I have never understood how it was that he got into such frightful financial difficulties. I can only imagine that Marian must have had, in one way or another, the greater portion of the income he got from the scholarships he held. I do know that his affection for her seemed at this time to be very sincere. And out of that affection there grew up, very naturally, a horror in his sensitive mind for the life this poor child was leading. He haunted the streets which she haunted, and sometimes saw her with other men. I suppose even then she must have been frightfully extravagant, and perhaps given to drink, but considering what his income was he should have been able to give her a pound a week if necessary, and yet have sufficient to live on without great difficulty. Nevertheless he did get into difficulties, and never even spoke to me about them. I was quite aware, in a dim kind of way, that he was in trouble and looked very ill, but he did not give me his fullest confidence, although one day he told me, as he had told Lake, that he proposed to marry her. I was only a boy, but I was absolutely enraged at the notion and used every possible means to prevent him from committing such an absurd act of folly. When we met I discussed it with him. I suppose I wrote him a dozen letters begging that he would do no such foolish thing. He would wrong himself, and could do the girl no possible good. My instincts told me even then that, instead of being raised, she would pull him down. These letters of mine were afterwards discovered in his rooms when the tragedy had happened.

During that time in 1876, we students at Moorhampton College were much disturbed by a series of thefts in the common room, and from a locker room in which we kept our books and papers and our overcoats. Books disappeared unaccountably and so did coats. Money was taken from the pockets of coats, and nobody knew who was to blame for it. Naturally enough we suspected a porter or one of the lower staff, but we were wrong. Without our knowledge the college authorities set a detective to discover the offender. One day I went into the common room, and standing in front of the fire found a man, a young fellow about my age, called Sarle,[1] with whom I frequently played chess— he was afterwards president of the Chess Club at Oxford—and he said to me : " Have you heard the news ? " " What news ? " I asked. " Your friend, Henry Maitland, has been stealing those things that we have lost," said he. And when he said so I very nearly struck him, for it seemed a gross and incredible slander. But unfortunately it was true, and at that very moment Maitland was in gaol. A detective had hidden himself in the small room leading out of the bigger room where the lockers were and had caught him in the act. It was a very ghastly business and certainly the first great shock I ever got in my life. I think it was the same for everybody who knew the boy. The whole college was in a most extraordinary ferment, and all the Moorhampton people who took any real interest in the institution.

[1] Probably Charles Taylor, admitted to Owens College, 1872 ; President of the Oxford Chess Club, 1879.

Professor Little, who was then the head of the college, sent for me and asked me what I knew of the matter. This was because the police had found in Maitland's room letters from me which referred to Marian Hilton. I told the professor with the utmost frankness everything I knew, and maintained that I had done my utmost to get him to break with her, a statement all my letters supported. I have often imagined a certain suspicion, in the minds of some of those who are given to suspicion, that I had myself been leading the same kind of life as Henry Maitland. This was certainly not true ; but one or two of those who did not like me—and there are always some—even threw out hints that I knew Maitland had been taking these things. Yet after my very painful interview with Professor Little, who was a very delightful and kindly personality—though certainly not so strong a man as the head of such a place should be—I saw that he gave me every credit for what I had tried to do. Among my own friends at the college was a young fellow, Edward Wolff, the son of the Rev. Mr. Wolff, the Unitarian minister at the chapel in Broad Street. Edward was afterwards fifth wrangler of his year at Cambridge. He induced his father to interest himself in Henry Maitland's future. Mr. Wolff and several other men of some eminence in the city did what they could for him. They got together a little money and on his release sent him away to America. He was met on coming out of prison by Dr. Lake's father, who also helped him in every possible way.

It seemed to me then that I had probably seen the last of Maitland, and the turn my own career took shortly afterwards rendered this even more likely. In the middle of 1876 I had a very serious disagreement with my father, who was a man of great ability but

very violent temper, and left home. On September 23
of that year I sailed for Australia and remained there,
working mostly in the bush, for the best part of three
years. During all that time I heard little of Henry
Maitland, though I have some dim remembrance of a
letter from him telling me that he was in America. It
was in 1879 that I shipped before the mast at Mel-
bourne in a Blackwall barque and came back to England
as a seaman.

## II

APSYCHOLOGIST or a romancer might comment on the matter of the last chapter till the sun went down, but the world perhaps would not be much further advanced. It is better for the man's apology or condemnation to come out of the drama that followed. This is where Life mocks at Art. The tragic climax and catastrophe are in the first act, and the remainder is a long and bitter commentary. Maitland and I seldom discussed his early life. Practically we never spoke of Moorhampton though we often enough touched on ancient things by implication. His whole life, as I saw it and shall relate it, is but a development of the nature which made his disaster possible.

So I come back to my own return from Australia. I had gone out there as a boy, and came back a man, for I had had a man's experiences ; work, adventure, travel, hunger, and thirst. All this hardened a somewhat neurotic temperament, at any rate for the time, till life in a city, and the humaner world of books removed the temper which one gets when plunged in the baths of the ocean. During some months I worked for a position in the Civil Service and thought very little of Maitland, for he was lost. Yet as I got back into the classics he recurred to me at times, and I wrote about him to my own friends in Moorhampton. They sent me vague reports of him in the United States, and then at last there came word that he was once more in England ; possibly, and even probably, in London. Soon afterwards I found in the *Athenæum* an advertisement of a book entitled " Children of the Dawn," [1] by Henry Maitland. As soon as I saw it I went straightway to the firm that published it, and being ignorant of the ways of publishers, demanded Maitland's address, which was promptly and very properly refused—for all they knew I might have been a creditor. They promised, however, to send on a letter to him, and I wrote at once, receiving an answer the very next day. He appointed as our meeting-place the smoking-room of the Horse Shoe Hotel at the bottom of Tottenham Court Road. It was probably one of the most curious meetings that had ever taken place in such a locality. We met late at night in the crowded smoking-room, and I found him very much his old self, for he was still a handsome and intelligent boy, though somewhat worn and haggard considering his years. He told me, chuckling, that I looked like a soldier, which was no doubt the result of some years on horseback—possibly I walked with a cavalry stride. We sat and drank coffee, and had whiskey, and smoked, until we were turned out of the hotel at half-past twelve. It was perhaps owing to the fact that I was ever the greater talker that he learnt more of my life in Australia than I learnt of his in the United States. He was, in fact, somewhat reserved about his adventures there. And yet, little by little, I learnt a great deal—it was always with him a case of little by little. At no time did he possess any great fluency or power of words when speaking of his own life.

It seems that friends had given him some letters to writers and others in New York, and he made the acquaintance there of many whose names I forget. I recollect only the name of Lloyd Garrison, the poet. Maitland told me that once Lloyd Garrison got him to go home with him about two o'clock in the morning to

[1] *Workers in the Dawn* (1880).

hear a sonnet on which Garrison had been working, as
he affirmed almost with tears, for three whole months.
As Maitland said, the result hardly justified the toil.
Among his new friends were some of artistic and literary
tendencies who had made a little club, where it was *de
rigueur* at certain times to produce something in the
form of a poem. Maitland showed me the set of verses
with which he had paid his literary footing ; they were
amusing, but of no great importance. So long as
Maitland's money lasted in New York he had not an
unpleasant time. It was only when he had exhausted
his means and had to earn a living by using his wits
that he found himself in great difficulties, which were
certainly not to be mitigated by the production of verse.
But Maitland never pretended to write poetry, though
he sometimes tried. I still have a few of his poems in
my possession, one of them a set of love verses which he
had put into a book but omitted on my most fervent
recommendation. I believe, however, that there is still
in existence much of his verse, if he did not destroy it
in later years when circumstances, his wanderings and
his poverty, made it inconvenient to preserve comparatively worthless papers. And yet, if he did not do
so, it might now be of no small interest to men of letters.

When his means were almost exhausted he went to
Boston, and from there drifted to Chicago. With a
very few additions and alterations, the account given
in " Paternoster Row " [1] would contain the essence of
Maitland's own adventures in America. It is, however,
written in a very light style, and is more or less tinged
with humour. This humour is purely literary, for he
felt very little of it when he was telling me the story.
He certainly lived during two days, for instance, upon
peanuts, and he did it in a town called Troy. I never

---

[1] *New Grub Street* (1891), chapter XXVIII.

gathered what actually drove him to Chicago : it was, perhaps, the general idea one gets in America that by going west one goes to the land of chances, but it certainly was not the place for Henry Maitland. As he relates in " Paternoster Row," he reached it with less than five dollars in his pocket, and with a courage at which he himself marvelled, paid four and a half dollars for a week's board and lodging, which made him secure for the moment. This boarding-house he once or twice described to me. It was an unclean place somewhere on Wabash Avenue, and was occupied very largely by small actors and hangers-on at the Chicago theatres. The food was poor, the service was worse, and there was only one common room in which they ate and lived. It was at this time, when he had taken a look round Chicago and found it very like Hell or Glasgow, which, indeed, it is, that he determined to attack the editor of the *Chicago Tribune*. The description he gives of this scene in " Paternoster Row " is not wholly accurate. I remember he said that he walked to and fro for hours outside the office of the paper before he took what remained of his courage in both hands, rushed into the elevator, and was carried to an upper storey. He asked for work, and the accessible and genial editor demanded, in return, what experience he had had of journalism. He said, with desperate bold-ness, " None whatever," and the editor, not at all un-kindly, asked him what he thought he could do for them. He replied, " There is one thing wanting in your paper." " What is that ? " asked the editor. " Fiction," said Maitland, " I should like to write you some." The editor considered the matter, and said that he had no objection to using a story provided it was good ; it would serve for one of the weekly sup-plements, because these American papers at the end of the week have amazing supplements, full of all conceivable sorts of matter, " litter," good, bad, and indifferent. Maitland asked if he might try him with a story of English life, and got permission to do so.

He went away and walked up and down the lake shore for hours in the bitter wind, trying to think out a story, and at last discovered one. On his way home he bought a pen, ink, and paper, which they did not supply at the boarding-house. As it was impossible to write in his bedroom where there was, of course, no fire, and no proper heating, it being so poor a place, he was compelled to write on the table of the common room with a dozen other men there, talking, smoking, and no doubt quarrelling. He wrote this story in a couple of days, and it was long enough to fill several columns of the paper. To his intense relief it was accepted by the editor after a day or two's waiting, and he got eighteen dollars according to " Paternoster Row," though I believe as a matter of fact it was less in reality. He stayed for some time in Chicago working for the *Tribune*, but at last found that he could write no more. I believe the editor himself suggested that the stories were perhaps not quite what he wanted. The one that I saw I only remember vaguely. It was, however, a sort of psychological love-story placed in London, written without much distinction.

The account Broughton [1] gives in " Paternoster Row " of his visit to Troy is also fairly representative of Maitland's experiences. It was there that he lived for two or three days on peanuts, now and then buying five cents' worth in the street at some Italian peanut stand. In " Paternoster Row " he calls them loathsome, and no doubt they soon do become disagreeable. A few are rather pleasing, more than a few are objection-

[1] Whelpdale.

able ; and when anybody tries a whole diet of them
for a day or two there is no doubt " loathsome " would
be the proper word. After that he worked a few days
for a photographer, and then, I think, for a plumber,
but of this I remember very little.[1] It is quite certain
that he never earned enough money in America to
enable him to return to England, but who lent it to
him I have no idea. To have been twenty-four hours
with no more than a handful of peanuts in his pocket
was no doubt unpleasant, but, as I told him, it seemed
very little to me. On one occasion in Australia I had
been rather more than four and a half days without
food when caught in a flood. Nevertheless this starvation was for him one of the initiation ceremonies into
the mysteries of literature, and he was always accustomed
to say, " How can such an one write ? He never
starved."

Still, to have been hard up in Chicago was a very
great experience, as every one knows who knows that
roaring city of the plains. Since that time I got to
know Chicago well, and was there " dead broke."
Thus I can imagine the state that he must have been
in, and how desperate he must have become, to get
out of his difficulties in the way he describes. The
endeavour to obtain work in a hustling country like
the United States is ever a desperate proceeding for a
nervous and sensitive man, and what it must have been
to Henry Maitland to do what he did with the editor
of the *Chicago Tribune* can only be imagined by those
who knew him. In many ways he was the most modest
and the shyest man who ever lived, and yet he actually
told this editor : " I have come to point out to you
there is a serious lack in your paper." To those who
knew Maitland this must seem as surprising as it did

[1] Dr. M. C. Donnelly, writing in America, repudiates the plumber.

to myself, and in later years he sometimes thought of that incident with inexpressible joy at his own courage. Of course the oddest thing about the whole affair is that up to that moment he had never written fiction at all, and only did so because he was driven to desperation. As will be seen when I come later to discuss his qualifications as a writer this is a curious comment on much of his bigger work. To me it seems that he should never have written fiction at all, although he did it so admirably. I think it would be very interesting if some American student of Maitland would turn over the files of the *Tribune* in the year 1877 and disinter the work he did there.[1] This is practically all I ever learnt about his life on the other side of the Atlantic. I was, indeed, more anxious to discover how he lived in London, and in what circumstances. I asked him as delicately as possible about his domestic circumstances, and he then told me that he was married, and that his wife was with him in London.

It is very curious that I never met his first wife. I had seen her photograph, and on several occasions was in the next room to her. On those occasions she was usually unfit to be seen, because she was intoxicated. When we renewed our acquaintance in the Horse Shoe Tavern he was living in mean apartments in one of the back streets off Tottenham Court Road not very far from the hotel and, indeed, not far from a cellar that he once occupied in a neighbouring street. Little by little, as I met him again and again, I began to get some hold upon his actual life. Gradually he became more confidential, and I gathered from him that the habits of his wife were perpetually compelling him to move from one house to another. From what he told me, sometimes hopefully, and more often in desperation,

[1] See Appendix B (*R.*).

it seems that this poor creature made vain and violent efforts to reform, generally after some long debauch. And of this I am very sure, that no man on earth could have made more desperate efforts to help her than he did. But the fact remains that they were turned out of one lodging after another, for even the poorest places, it seems, could hardly stand a woman of her character in the house. I fear it was not only that she drank but that at intervals she deserted him and went back, for the sake of more drink and for the sake of money with which he was unable to supply her, to her old melancholy trade. And yet she returned again with tears, and he took her in, doing his best for her. It was six months after our first meeting in Tottenham Court Road that he asked me to go and spend an evening with him. Naturally enough I then expected to make Mrs. Maitland's acquaintance, but on my arrival he showed some disturbance of mind and told me that she was ill and would be unable to see me. The house they lived in then was not very far from Morning-ton Crescent. It was certainly in some dull neighbour-hood not half a mile away. The street was, I think, a cul-de-sac. It was full of children of the lower orders playing in the roadway. It being Saturday night, their fathers and mothers sat upon the doorsteps, or quarrelled, or talked in the road. The front room in which he received me was both mean and dirty. The servant who took me upstairs was a poor foul slut, and I do not think the room had been properly cleaned or dusted for a very long time. The whole of the furniture in it was certainly not worth seven and sixpence from the point of view of the ordinary furniture dealer. There were signs in it that it had been occupied by a woman, and one without the common elements of decency and cleanliness. Under a miserable and broken sofa lay a pair of dirty feminine boots. And yet on one set of poor shelves there were, still shining with gold, the prizes Maitland had won at Moorhampton College, and the painfully acquired later stock of books that he loved so much.

As I came in by arrangement after my own dinner, we simply sat and smoked and drank a little whiskey. Twice in the course of an hour our conversation was interrupted by the servant knocking at the door and beckoning to Maitland to come out. In the next room I then heard voices, sometimes raised, sometimes pleading. When Maitland returned the first time he said to me, " I am very sorry to have to leave you for a few minutes. My wife is really unwell." But I knew by now the disease from which she suffered. Twice or thrice I was within an ace of getting up and saying, " Don't you think I'd better go, old chap ? " And then he was called out again. He came back at last in a state of obvious misery and perturbation, and said, " My dear man, my wife is so ill that I think I must ask you to go." I shook hands with him in silence and went, for I understood. A little afterwards he told me that that very afternoon his wife had gone out, and obtaining drink in some way had brought it home with her, and that she was then almost insane with alcohol. This was the kind of life that Henry Maitland, perhaps a great man of letters, lived for years. Comfortable people talk of his pessimism, and his greyness of outlook, and never understand. The man really was a hedonist, he loved things beautiful—beautiful and orderly. He rejoiced in every form of Art, in books and in music, and in all the finer inheritance of the past. But this was the life he lived, and the life he seemed to be doomed to live from the very first.

When a weak man has a powerful sense of duty he

is hard to handle by those who have some wisdom. I had done my best to induce him to give up this woman in the early days, long before he married her, when he was but a foolish boy. Now once more I did my best to get him to leave her, but cannot pretend for an instant that anything I said or did would have had any grave effect if it had not been that the poor woman was herself doomed to be her own destroyer. Her outbreaks became more frequent, her departures from his miserable roof more prolonged. The windy gaslight of the slums appealed to her, and the money that she earned therein ; and finally when it seemed that she would return no more he changed his rooms and, through the landlady of the wretched house at which he found she was staying, arranged to pay her ten shillings a week. As I know, he often made less than ten shillings a week, and sometimes found himself starving that she might have so much more to spend in drink.

This went on for years. It was still going on in 1884 when I left England again and went out to Texas. I had failed to make a successful attack upon the English Civil Service, and the hateful work done afterwards caused my health to break down. I was in America for three years, and during that time wrote fully and with a certain regularity to Maitland. When I came back and was writing " The Western Trail," [1] he returned me the letters he had received from me. Among them were some, frequently dealing with literary subjects, addressed from Texas, Minnesota, Iowa, the Rocky Mountains, British Columbia, Oregon, and California. In his letters to me he never referred to Marian, but I gathered that his life was very hard, and understood, without his saying it, that he was still supporting her. I found that this was so when I

[1] *The Western Avernus* (1887).

returned to England in 1887. At that time, by dint of hard laborious work, which included a great deal of teaching, he was making for the first time something of a living. He occupied a respectable but very dismal flat somewhere at the back of Madame Tussaud's, in a place at that time called " Cumberland Residences." [1] It was afterwards renamed " Cumberland Mansions," and I well remember Maitland's frightful and really superfluous scorn of the snobbery which spoke in such a change of name. As I said, we corresponded during the whole of the time I was in America. It is, from any point of view, a very great disaster that in some way, which I cannot account for, I have lost all his letters written to me previous to 1894. Our prolonged, and practically uninterrupted correspondence began in 1884, so I have actually lost the letters of ten whole years. They were interesting from many points of view. Much to my surprise, while I was in America, they came to me, not dated in the ordinary way, but according to the Comtist Calendar. I wrote to him for an explanation, because up to that time I had never heard of it. In his answering letter he told me that he had become a Positivist. This was doubtless owing to the fact that he had come accidentally under the influence of some well-known Positivists.

It seems that in desperation at his utter failure to make a real living at literature he had taken again to a tutor's work, which in a way was where he began. In his marriage certificate he called himself a teacher of languages. But he loathed teaching save in those rare instances where he had an intelligent and enthusiastic pupil. At the time that I came back to England he was teaching Harold Edgeworth's [2] sons.

[1] " Cornwall Residences," later " Cornwall Mansions."
[2] Frederic Harrison (1831–1923).

Without a doubt Harold Edgeworth was extremely kind to Henry Maitland and perhaps to some little extent appreciated him, in spite of the preface he wrote in later years to the posthumous "Basil." [1] Maitland was not only tutor to Harold Edgeworth's sons, but was also received at his house as a guest. He met there many men of a certain literary eminence ; Cotter Morison, for instance, of whom he sometimes spoke to me, especially of his once characterising a social chatterer as a *cloaca maxima* of small talk. He also met Edmund Roden,[2] with whom he remained on terms of friendship to the last, often visiting him in his house at Felixstowe,[3] which is known to many men of letters. I think the fact that Edmund Roden was not only a man of letters but also, oddly enough, the secretary of a great business, appealed in some way to Maitland's sense of humour. He liked Roden amazingly, and it was through him, if I remember rightly, that he became socially acquainted with George Meredith, whom, however, he had met in a business way when Meredith was reading for a firm of publishers [4] at a salary of two hundred a year.[5]

Nevertheless, in spite of his making money by some tutorial work, Maitland was still as poor as a rat in a cellar, and the absurd antinomy between the society he frequented at times and his real position made him sometimes shout with laughter which was not always really humorous. It was during this period of his life that a lady asked him at an "at-home" what his experience was in the management of butlers. According-ing to what he told me he replied seriously that he always strictly refrained from having anything to do with men-servants, as he much preferred a smart-

---

[1] *Veranilda* (1904).    [2] Edward Clodd (1840–1930).
[3] Aldeburgh.    [4] Chapman & Hall.    [5] Actually, I think, £250.

looking young maid. It was during this period that he did some work with a man employed, I think, at the London Skin Hospital. This poor fellow, it seemed, possessed ambition and desired to rise in life. He wanted to pass the London matriculation examination and thus become, as he imagined, somebody of importance. Naturally enough, being but a clerk, he lacked time for work, and the arrangement come to between him and Maitland was that his teacher should go to his lodgings at seven o'clock in the morning and give him his lesson in bed before breakfast. As this was just before the time that Maitland worked for Harold Edgeworth, he was too poor, so he said, to pay bus fares from the slum in which he lived, and consequently he had to rise at six o'clock in the morning, walk for a whole hour to his pupil's lodgings, and then was very frequently met with the message that Mr. So-and-so felt much too tired that morning to receive him. It is a curious comment on the authority of " The Meditations of Mark Sumner," [1] which many cling to as undoubtedly authentic, that he mentions this incident as if he did not mind it. As a matter of fact he was furiously wroth with this man for not rising to receive him, and used to go away in a state of almost ungovernable rage, as he told me many and many a time.

After my return from America we began to meet regularly once a week on Sunday afternoons, for I had now commenced my own initiation into the mystery of letters, and had become an author. By Maitland's advice, and, if I may say so, almost by his inspiration— most certainly his encouragement—I wrote " The Western Trail," and, having actually printed a book, felt that there was still another bond between me and

[1] *The Private Papers of Henry Ryecroft* (1903). The passage referred to is at " Summer," XI.

Maitland. I used to turn up regularly at 7 K Cumberland Residences at three o'clock on Sundays. From then till seven we talked of our work, of Latin and of Greek, of French, and of everything on earth that touched on literature. Long before seven Maitland used to apply himself very seriously to the subject of dinner. As he could not afford two fires he usually cooked his pot on the fire of the sitting-room. This pot of his was a great institution. It reminds me sometimes of the gypsies' pot in which they put everything that comes to hand. Maitland's idea of cooking was fatness and a certain amount of gross abundance. He would put into this pot potatoes, carrots, turnips, portions of meat, perhaps a steak, or on great days a whole rabbit, all of which he himself had bought, and carried home with his own hands. We used to watch the pot boiling, and perhaps about seven or half-past he would investigate its contents with a long two-pronged iron fork, and finally decide much to our joy and contentment that the contents were edible. After our meal, for which I was usually ready, as I was myself practically starving much of this time, we removed the débris, washed up in company, and resumed our literary conversation, which sometimes lasted until ten or eleven. By that time Maitland usually turned me out, although my own day was not necessarily done for several hours.

Those were great talks, but they were nearly always about ancient times, and of the Greeks and Romans, so far as we strayed from English literature. It may seem odd, and it *is* odd until it is explained, that he took very little interest in the Renaissance. There is still in existence a letter of his to Edmund Roden saying how much he regretted that he took no interest in it. That letter was, I think, dated from Siena, a city of the Renaissance. The truth of the matter is that he was himself essentially a creature of the Renaissance, a pure Humanist. For this very reason he displayed no particular pleasure in that period. He was interested in the time in which the men of the Renaissance revelled after the re-discovery and new birth of learning. He would have been at his best if he had been born when that time was in flower. The fathers of the Renaissance re-discovered Rome and Athens, and so did he. No one can persuade me that if this had been his fate his name would not now have been as sacred to all who love literature as those of Petrarch and his glorious fellows. As a matter of fact it was this very quality of his which gave him such a lofty and lordly contempt for the obscurantist theologian. In my mind I can see him treating, with that irony which was ever his favourite weapon, some relic of the dark ages of the schools. In those hours that we spent together it was wonderful to hear him talk of Greece even before he knew it, for he saw it as it had been, or as his mind made him think it had been, not with the modern Greek—who is perhaps not a Greek at all—shouting in the market-place. I think that he had a historical imagination of a very high order, even though he undoubtedly failed when endeavouring to use it. That was because he used it in the wrong medium. But when he saw the Acropolis in his mind he saw it before the Turks had stabled their horses in the Parthenon, and before the English, worse vandals than the Turks, had brought away to the biting smoke of London the marbles of Pheidias. Even as a boy he loved the roar and fume of Rome, although he had not yet seen it and could only imagine it. He saw in Italy the land of Dante and Boccaccio, a land still peopled in the south towards Sicily with such folks as these and Horace and Theocritus had known.

My own education had been wrought out in strange rough places in the new lands. It was a fresh education for me to come back to London and sit with Maitland on these marvellous Sunday afternoons and evenings when he wondered if the time would ever come for him to see Italy and Greece in all reality. It was for the little touches of realism, the little pictures in the Odes, that he loved Horace, and loved still more his Virgil; and, even more, Theocritus and Moschus, for Theocritus wrote things which were ancient and yet modern, full of the truth of humanity. Like all the men of the Renaissance he turned his eyes wistfully to the immemorial past, renewed in the magical alembic of his own mind.

Nevertheless, great as these hours were that we spent together, they were sometimes deeply melancholy, and he had nothing to console him for the miseries that were ever in the background. It was upon one of these Sundays, I think early in January [1] 1888, that I found him in a peculiarly melancholy and desperate condition. No doubt he was overworked, for he was always overworked ; but he said that he could stand it no longer, he must get out of London for a few days or so. For some reason, which I cannot for the world understand, he decided to go to Eastbourne, and begged me to go with him. Why he should have selected, in Christmas weather and an east wind, what is possibly the coldest town in England in such conditions, I cannot say, but I remember that the journey down to the sea was mercilessly cold. Of course we went third class, and the carriages were totally unheated. We were both of us practically in extreme poverty. I was living in a single room in Chelsea, for which I paid four shillings a week, and for many months my total weekly expenses

[1] Actually it was not until February 13 that Gissing went to Eastbourne.

were something under twelve shillings. At that particular moment he was doing extremely badly, and the ten shillings that he paid regularly to his wife frequently left him with insufficient to live upon. I can hardly understand how it was that he determined to spend even the little extra money needed for such a journey. When we reached Eastbourne we walked down to the sea front with our bags in our hands, and then, going into a poor back street, selected rooms.[1] It was, perhaps, due to what he and I often called " the native malignity of matter," and his extreme ill luck in the matter of landladies, which pursued him for ever throughout his life in lodgings, that the particular landlady of the house in which we took refuge was more than commonly incapable. The dwelling itself was miserably draughty and cold, and wretchedly furnished. The east wind which blows over the flat marshes between Eastbourne and the Downs entered the house at every crack, and there were many of them. The first night we were in the town it snowed very heavily, and in our shabby little sitting-room we shivered in spite of the starved fire. We sat there with our overcoats on and did our best to be cheerful. Heaven alone knows what we talked of, but most likely, and very possibly, it may have been Greek metres, always his great passion. Yet neither of us was in good case. We both had trouble enough on our shoulders. I remember that he spoke very little of his wife, for I would not let him do so, although I knew she was most tremendously on his mind, and was, in fact, what had driven him for the moment out of London. Of course, he had a very natural desire that she might die and have done with life, with the life which must have been a torment to herself as it was a perpetual torture and a running sore

[1] At 27 Brightland Road.

to him. At the same time the poor fellow felt that he had no right to wish that she would die, but I could see the thought in his eyes, and heaven knows that I wished it fervently for him.

The next morning [1] we went for a long walk across the Downs to the little village of East Dean. It was blowing a whole gale from the north-east, and it was quite impossible to go near the steep cliffs. The snow was in places two feet deep, and a sunk road across the Downs was level with the turf. I think now that none but madmen would have gone out on such a day. Doubtless we were mad enough ; at any rate we were writers, and by all traditions had the right to be mad. But when we once got started we meant going through it at all events. I did not remember many colder days, in spite of my travels, but we persevered, and at last came to the little village and there took refuge in the public-house and drank beer. Maitland, with his extraordinary mixture of fine taste and something which was almost grossness in regard to food, loved all malt liquors—I think partly because he felt some strange charm in their being historically English drinks. The walk back to Eastbourne tried us both hard, for neither of us had been well fed for months, and the wind and snow in our faces made walking heavy and difficult. Nevertheless Maitland was now almost boisterously cheerful, as he often was outwardly when he had most reason to be the opposite. While he walked back the chief topic of conversation was the very excellent nature of the pudding which he had instructed our landlady to prepare against a hungry return.

He was always peculiarly fond of rich, succulent dishes. A *fritto misto* for instance, made him shout for joy, though he never met with one until he went to

[1] February 16, in fact.

Italy. With what inimitable fervour of the gastronomic mind would he declare these preferences ! Dr.
Johnson said that in a haggis there was much " fine,
confused feeding," [1] and Maitland undoubtedly agreed
with him, as he always said when he quoted the passage.
In many of his books there are examples of his curious
feeling with regard to food. They are especially
frequent in " Paternoster Row " ; as, for instance,
when one character says : " Better dripping this than
I've had for a long time. . . . Now, with a little
pepper and salt, this bread and dripping is as appetising
a food as I know. I often make a dinner of it." To
which the other replies : " I have done the same myself
before now. Do you ever buy pease-pudding ? " and
to this the Irishman's reply was enthusiastic. " I
should think so ! I get magnificent pennyworths at a
shop in Cleveland Street, of a very rich quality indeed.
Excellent faggots they have there, too. I'll give you a
supper of them one night before you go." I had often
heard of this particular place in Cleveland Street, and
of one shop where they sold beef, kept by a man whose
pride was that he had been carving behind the counter
for thirty years without a holiday.

And now we were hurrying back to Eastbourne,
Maitland said, not because it was cold ; not because
the north-east wind blew ; not because we were exposed
to the very bitterest weather we remembered ; but
because of an exceedingly rich compound known as
an apple pudding. He and the wind worked me up to
an almost equal expression of ardour, and thus we came

[1] It is perhaps worth noting that this phrase properly belongs to Dr. John
Brown and that the victual in question was a singed sheep's head. The passage
is in the essay " With brains, Sir ", in *Horæ Subsecivæ*, and tells how a Scotsman,
being called to account for describing this delicacy as a *dish*, replied : " Dish or
no dish, there's a deal o' fine confused feedin' aboot it, let me tell you."
    Dr. Johnson also encountered a sheep's head at breakfast at Moy—hence, no
doubt, the confusion.

back to our poverty-stricken den in good spirits. But, alas, the dinner that day was actually disastrous. The meat was grossly overdone, the vegetables were badly cooked, the beer was thin and flat. We were in dismay, but still we said to each other hopefully that there was the pudding to come. It was brought on and looked very fine, and Maitland cut into it with great joy and gave me a generous helping. I know that I tasted it eagerly, but to my tongue there was an alien flavour about it. I looked up and said to Maitland, " It is very curious, but this pudding seems to me to taste of kerosene." Maitland laughed, but when his turn came to try he laughed no longer, for the pudding actually did taste of lamp oil. It appeared, on plaintive and bitter inquiry, that our unfortunate landlady after making it had put it under the shelf on which she kept her lamp gear. We subsided on melancholy and mouldy cheese. This disappointment, however childish it may appear to the better fed, was to Henry Maitland something really serious. Those who have read " The Meditations of Mark Sumner," without falling into the error of thinking that the talk about food in that melancholy book was only his fun, will understand that it was a very serious matter with Maitland. It took all his philosophy and a very great deal of mine to survive the tragedy, and to go on talking as we did of new words and the riches of philology. And as we talked the wind roared down our street in a vicious frenzy. It was a monstrously bad time to have come to Eastbourne, and we had no compensations.

It was the next night that the great news came. In spite of the dreariest weather we had spent most of the day in the open air. After our dinner, which this time was more of a success, or at any rate less of a tragic failure, we were sitting hugging the fire to keep warm

when a telegram was brought in for him. He read it
in silence and handed it over to me with the very
strangest look upon his face that I had ever seen. It
was unsigned, and came from London. The message
was : " Your wife is dead." [1]  There was nothing on
earth more desirable for him than that she might die,
the poor wretch truly being like a destructive wind, for
she had torn his heart, scorched his very soul, and
destroyed him at the beginning of his life. All irreparable disasters came from her, and through her. Had it
not been for her he might then have held, or have
begun to hope for, a great position at one of the universities. And now a voice out of the unknown cried that
she was dead.

He said to me, with a shaking voice and shaking
hands, " I cannot believe it—I cannot believe it." He
was as white as paper ; for it meant so much—not only
freedom from the disaster and shame and misery that
drained his life-blood, but it would mean a cessation of
money payments at a time when every shilling was
very hard to win. And yet this was when he was
comparatively well known, for it was two years after
the publication of " The Mob." [2]  And still, though his
books ran into many editions, for some inexplicable
reason, which I yet hope to explain, he sold them one
after another for fifty pounds. And I knew how he
worked ; how hard, how remorselessly. I knew who
the chief character was in " Paternoster Row " before
" Paternoster Row " was written. I knew with what
inexpressible anguish of soul he laboured, with what
dumb rage against destiny. And now here was something like freedom at last, if only this were true.

[1] Roberts, in this passage, has let his dramatic sense get the better of him.
It was not until February 29 that the telegram arrived. Gissing was then alone,
and at once telegraphed to Roberts to meet him in London that night.
[2] *Demos* (1886).

The message came so late at night that there was no possibility of telegraphing to London to verify it even if he had been sure that he could get to the original sender. It was also much too late to go up to town. We sat silently for hours, and I knew that he was going back over the burning marl of the past. Sometimes he did speak, asking once and again if it could be true, and I saw that while he was still uncertain he was bitter and pitiless. Yet if only she were really dead . . .

We went up to town together in the morning. In the train he told me that, while he was still uncertain, he could not possibly visit the place she lived in, so he begged me to go there straight and bring him word as to the truth of this report. I was to explore the desperate slum in the New Cut in which she had exhausted the last dreadful years of her life, and upon leaving him I went there at once. With Maitland's full permission I described something of the milieu in " John Quest." [1] On reaching the New Cut I dived into an inner slum from an outer one, and at last found myself in a kitchen which was only about eight or nine feet square. It was, of course, exceedingly dirty. The person in charge of it was a cheerful red-headed girl of about eighteen years of age. On learning the cause of my visit she went out and brought in her mother, and I soon verified the fact that Marian Maitland was dead. She had died the first bitter night we spent at Eastbourne,[2] and was found next morning without any blankets, and with no covering for her emaciated body but a damp and draggled gown.

Presently the neighbours came in to see the gentleman who was interested in this woman's death. They talked eagerly of the funeral, for, as Maitland knew

---

[1] *Maurice Quain* (1897).

[2] Here, again, Roberts has distorted, by dramatization, the actual time-scheme of his events.

only too well, a funeral, to these people, is one of their great irregular but recurring festivals. At Maitland's desire I gave them *carte blanche* up to a certain sum, and I think they felt that, as the agent of the husband, I behaved very well. Of course they knew all about the poor girl who lay dead upstairs, and although they were honest enough people in their way, and though the red-headed girl to whom I first talked worked hard in a factory making hooks and eyes, as she told me, they seemed to have no moral feelings whatever about her very obvious profession. I myself did not see the dead woman. I was not then acquainted with death, save among strangers. I could not bring myself to look upon her. Although death is so dreadful always, the surroundings of death may make things worse. But still, she *was* dead, and I hastened back to Maitland to tell him so. It was a terrible and painful relief to him ; and when he was sure she was gone, he grieved for her, grieved for what she might have been, and for what she was. He remembered now that at intervals she used to send him heart-breaking messages asking to be forgiven, messages that even his unwisdom at last could not listen to. But he said very little. So far as the expression of his emotions went he often had very great self-control. It is a pity that his self-control so rarely extended itself to acts. But now he was free. Those who have forged their own chains, and lived in a hell of their own dreadful making, can understand what this is and what it means. But he did go down to the pit in which she died, and when I saw him a day or two later he was strangely quiet, even for him. He said to me, " My dear chap, she had kept my photograph, and a very little engraving of the Madonna di San Sisto, all these years of horrible degradation." He spoke in the almost inaudible tone that was characteristic of him, especially at that time. We arranged the funeral together, and she was buried. If only all the misery that she had caused him could have been buried with her, it would have been well. She died of what I may call, euphemistically, specific laryngitis. Once he told me a dreadful story about her in hospital. One of the doctors at St. Thomas's had questioned her, and after her answers sent for Maitland, and speaking to him on the information given him by the wife, was very bitter. Henry, even as he told me of this years after, shook with rage and indignation. He had not been able to defend himself without exposing his wife's career.

# III

THERE are many methods of writing biography. Each has its advantages, even the chronological compilation. But chronology is no strong point of mine, and in this sketch I shall lay but little stress on dates. There is great advantage in describing things as they impress themselves on the writer. A portrait gains in coherency and completeness by temporary omissions more than it can ever gain by the empty endeavour to handle each period fully. In this last chapter I might have endeavoured to describe Maitland at work, or to speak of his ambitions, or even to criticise what he had already done, or to give my own views of what he meant to achieve. There is authority for every method, and most authorities are bad, save Boswell—and few would pine for Boswell's qualities at the price of his failings. Yet one gets help from him everywhere, little as it may show. Only the other day I came across a passage in the " Journal of a Tour to the Hebrides " [1] which has some value. Reporting Johnson, he writes : " Talking of biography, he said he did not think the life of any literary man in England had been well written. Besides the common incidents of life it should tell us his studies, his mode of living, the means by which he attained to excellence, and his opinion of his own works." Such I shall endeavour to do. Nevertheless Johnson was wrong. Good work had then been done in biography by Walton, whose Lives, by the way, Maitland loved ; and Johnson himself was

[1] Under September 22, 1773.

not far from great excellence when he described his friend Savage in the " Lives of Poets " in spite of his want of colloquial ease. There came in then the value of friendship and actual personal knowledge, as it did in Boswell's " Life." I can only hope that my own deep acquaintance with Maitland will compensate for my want of skill in the art of writing lives, for which novel-writing is but a poor training. Yet the deeper one's knowledge the better it is to simplify as one goes, taking things by themselves, going forwards or backwards as may seem best, without care of tradition, especially where tradition is mostly bad. We do not now write biography in England as Romain Rolland wrote that of Beethoven. Seldom are we grieved for our heroes, or rejoice with them. Photography, or the photographic portrait, is more in request than an impression. However, let me resume in my own way, having to be content with that, and caring little for opinion, that fluctuant critic.

Long as our friendship existed it is perhaps curious that we never called each other, except on very rare occasions, by anything but our surnames. This, I think, is due to the fact that we had been at Moorhampton College together. It is, I imagine, the same thing with most schoolboys. Provided there is no nickname given, men who have been chums at school seem to prefer the surname by which they knew their friends in the early days. I have often noticed there is a certain savage tendency on the part of boys to suppress their Christian names, their own peculiar mark. And sometimes I have wondered whether this is not in some obscure way a survival of the savage custom of many tribes in which nobody is ever mentioned by his right name, because in that name there inheres mysteriously the very essence of his being and inheritance, the knowledge of which by others may expose him to some occult danger.

I said above that from the time I first met Maitland after my return from Australia, until I went away again to Arizona,[1] I was working in the Admiralty[2] and the India Office as a writer at tenpence an hour. The pay was exiguous, and my prospects worth nothing. Yet when I came back from America and found him domiciled at 7 K Cumberland Residences, my economic basis in life became even more exiguous, whatever hope might have said of my literary future. I was even poorer than Maitland. He lived in a flat and had at least two rooms and a kitchen. Yet it was a horrible place of extraordinary gloom, and its back windows overlooked the roaring steam engines of the Metropolitan Railway. No doubt my own apartment, when I took to living by myself, was superior in cheerfulness to 7 K. Shortly after my return to England, I hired a single room in Chelsea, put in a few sticks of furniture given to me by my people, and began housekeeping on my own account on all I could make and the temporary ten shillings a week allowed me by my father, who at that time, for all his native respect for literature, regarded the practice of it with small hope and much suspicion. I know that it greatly amused Maitland to hear of his views on the subject of the self-revelations in " The Western Trail," which dealt with my life in Western America. After reading that book he did not speak to me for three days, and told my younger brother, " These are pretty revelations about your brother having been a common loafer." At this Maitland roared, but he roared none the less when he understood that three columns of laudation in one of the reviews entirely changed my father's view of that particular book.

[1] Texas.　　　　[2] Actually the War Office.

I should not trouble to say anything about my own particular surroundings if it were not that in a sense they also became Maitland's, although I went more frequently to him than he came to me. Nevertheless he was quite familiar with my one room and often had meals there which I cooked for him. Of course at that time, from one point of view, I was but a literary beginner and aspirant, while Maitland was a rising and respected man, who certainly might be poor, and was poor, but still he had published " The Mob " and other books, his name was well known, and his prospects, from the literary, if not from the financial point of view, seemed very good. I was the author of one book, the result of three years' bitter hard experience, written in twenty-six days as a *tour de force*, and though I had ambition I seemed to have nothing more to write about. From my own point of view Maitland was, of course, very successful. His flat with more rooms than one in it was a mansion, and he was certainly making something like a hundred a year. Still, I think that when he came down to me and found me comparatively independent, he rather envied me. At any rate I had not to keep an errant wife on money made with infinite difficulty. He came to see me in Chelsea in my very early days, and took great joy in my conditions. For one thing I had no attendance with this room. I was supposed to look after it for myself in every way. This, he assured me, made my estate the more gracious, as anyone can understand who remembers all that he has said about landladies and lodging-house servants and charwomen. He chuckled over the list of things I bought : a fender and fire-irons, a coal-scuttle, a dust-bin, and blacking brushes. He found me one day shaving by the aid of my own dim reflection in the glass of an etching which I had brought from home, because I had no looking-glass and no money to spare for one. We frequently went together over the question of finance. Incidentally I found his own habit of buying cooked meat peculiarly extravagant. There is still a book among my papers in which I kept accounts for my first three months in Chelsea to see how one could live on ten shillings a week, which Maitland assured me was preposterous riches, even if I managed to make no more.

Naturally enough, seeing that we had been friends for so long, and seeing that he had encouraged me so greatly to write my first book, he took a vast interest in all my proceedings, and was very " joyous," as he would have said, to observe that I could not afford sheets but slept in the blankets which I had carried all over America. I seek no sympathy on this point, for after all it was not a matter of my being unable to afford linen ; it is impossible for the average comfortable citizen to understand how disagreeable sheets become after some thousands of nights spent camping in mere wool, even of the cheapest. It took me years to learn to resign myself to cold linen, or even more sympathetic cotton, when I became a respectable householder.

In the neighbourhood where I then lived there is a great artistic colony, and as I already knew one or two artists, I soon became acquainted with all the others. Many of them were no richer than myself, and as Bohemia and the belief that there was still a Bohemia formed one of Maitland's greatest joys, he was always delighted to hear of any of our remarkable shifts to live. It is an odd thing to reflect that A. D. Mack,[1] Frank Wynne, Albert Croft, three other artists whose names I now forget and I once had a glorious supper of fried fish served in a newspaper on the floor of an empty

[1] A. D. M'Cormick, (1860–1943).

studio. The only thing missing on that particular occasion was Maitland's presence, but, of course, the trouble was that Maitland would seldom associate with anybody whom he did not know already, and I could rarely get him to make the acquaintance of my own friends. Yet such experiences as we were sometimes reduced to more than proved to him that his dear Bohemia existed, though later in his life, as one sees in " Mark Sumner," he often seemed to doubt whether it was still extant. On this point I used to console him, saying that where any two artists butt their foolish heads against the economic system, there is Bohemia ; Bohemia, in fact, is living on a course of high ideals, whatever the world says of them. At this hour there are writers learning their business on a little oatmeal, as George Meredith did, or destroying their digestions, as I did mine and Henry Maitland's, on canned corned beef. Even now, perhaps, some writers and artists are making their one big meal a day on fried fish.

One Sunday I missed going to Maitland's, because he was then out of town visiting his family, but I had a tale for him on his return. It seems that I had been writing, and had got so disgusted with the result that I could not possibly stay in my room, so determined to go round to my friend Mack. No sooner had I made up my mind on this subject than there was a knock at the door, and presently in came Mack himself. I said promptly, " It is no good your coming here, for I was just going round to you." Whereupon he replied, " It is no good your coming to me because I have no coal, no coke, and nobody will give me any more because I owe for so much already." I replied that I was not going to stay in my room in any case, and affirmed that I would rather be in his studio in the cold than where I was. Whereupon he suddenly discovered that my scuttle was actually full of coal, and proposed to take it round to the studio. This seemed a really brilliant idea, and after much discussion of ways and means my inventive faculty produced an old portmanteau and several newspapers, and after wrapping up lumps of coal in separate pieces of paper we packed the portmanteau with coal and carried it round to the studio in Manresa Road. This appeared to Maitland so characteristic of an artist's life that it seemed pure Murger.

In one matter Maitland and I were at that time much alike. From most points of view there can hardly have been two more different men, for he was essentially of the study and the cloister, while I was far more naturally a man of the open air. Nevertheless, when it came to journalism we were both of the same mind. While I was away from England and he was teaching Harold Edgeworth's sons, Edgeworth introduced him to John Harley,[1] then editing the *Piccadilly Gazette*,[2] who offered, no doubt seriously, to use as much matter as possible if Maitland would supply him with something in journalistic form. Apparently he found it too much against his natural grain to do this work, and I was now in the same predicament. It is true that I had something of a natural journalistic flair which he lacked, but my nose for a likely article was rendered entirely useless to me by the fact that I never could write anything until I had thought about it for several days, by which time it was stale, and much too late from the newspaper point of view. However, Maitland occasionally did a little odd journalism, for I remember being with him before I went to America, when he received the proofs of an article from the *St. James's Gazette*, and picking up " Mark Sumner "[3] one

---

[1] John Morley (1838–1923).      [2] *Pall Mall Gazette.*
[3] *Henry Ryecroft :* " Autumn," XXI.

may read : " I thought of this as I sat yesterday watching a noble sunset, which brought back to my memory the sunsets of a London autumn, thirty years ago. It happened that, on one such evening, I was by the river at Chelsea, with nothing to do except to feel that I was hungry, and to reflect that, before morning, I should be hungrier still. I loitered upon Battersea Bridge—the old picturesque wooden bridge, and there the western sky took hold upon me. Half an hour later I was speeding home. I sat down, wrote a description of what I had seen, and straightway sent it to an evening paper, which, to my astonishment, published the thing next day—' On Battersea Bridge.' " I have never seen that article since I saw the proof of it, but there was something so characteristic in it that I think it would be worth some one's while to hunt up the files of the *St. James's Gazette* in order to find it. For while he was leaning over the bridge, enjoying the sunset, there was also a workman looking at it. The river was at a low stage, at least three-quarters-ebb, and on each side of it there were great patches of shining mud, in which the glorious western sky was reflected, turning the ooze into a mass of most wonderful colour. Maitland said to me, " Of course I was pleased to see somebody else, especially a poor fellow like that, enjoying the beauty of the sunset. But presently my companion edged a little closer to me, and seeing my eyes directed towards the mud which showed such heavenly colouring, he remarked to me, with an air of the deepest interest, ' Throws up an 'eap of mud, don't she ? ' "

Sometimes when Maitland came to me in Danvers Street he used to go over my accounts and discuss means of making them less. I think his chief joy in them was the feeling that some of his more respectable friends, such as Harold Edgeworth, would have been horrified at my peculiarly squalid existence. In a sense it was, no doubt, squalid, and yet in another it was perhaps the greatest time in my life, and Maitland knew it. In the little book in which I kept my expenses he came across one day on which I had spent absolutely nothing. This was a great treat for him. On another day he found a penny put down as "charity." On looking up the book I see that a note still declares that this penny was given to a little girl to pay her fare in the bus. This beneficence on my part necessitated my walking all the way to Chelsea from Hyde Park Corner. Yet Maitland assured me that, compared with himself at times, I was practically a millionaire, although he owned that he had very rarely beaten my record when all expenditure on food was but three-and-sixpence. One week it actually totalled no more than one-and-elevenpence, but I have no doubt that I went out to eat with somebody else on those days—unless it was at the time my liver protested against the life I led, and gave me such an attack of gloom that I went to bed and lay there for three days without eating, firmly determined to die and have done with the literary struggle. This fast did me a great deal of good. On the fourth day I got up and rustled vigorously for a meal, and did some financing with the admirable result of producing a whole half-crown.

Whenever Maitland came I cooked his food and my own on a little grid, or in a frying-pan, over the fire in my one room. The fire cost me on an average a whole shilling a week, or perhaps a penny or two more if the coal, which I bought in the street, went up in price. This means that I ran a fire on a hundredweight of coal each week, or sixteen pounds of coal a day. Maitland, who was an expert in coal, assured me that I was extremely extravagant, and that a fire could be kept going for much less. On trying, I found out that when I was exceedingly hard up I could keep in a very little fire for several hours a day on only eight pounds of coal, but sometimes I had to let it go out, and run round to a studio to get warm by some artist's stove—provided always that the merchant in coke who supplied him had not refused any further credit.

At this time Maitland and I were both accustomed to work late, although he was just then beginning to labour at more reasonable times, though not to write fewer hours. I used to find getting up in the morning at a proper hour quite impossible. Probably this was due to some inherited gout, to poisonous indigestion from my own cooking, or to a continued diet of desiccated soups and " Jungle " beef from Chicago. However, it seemed to Maitland that I was quite in the proper tradition of letters while I was working on a long novel, only published years afterwards, which I used to begin at ten or eleven o'clock at night, frequently finishing at six o'clock in the morning when the sparrows began to chirp outside my window.

As a result of this night-work I used to get up at four o'clock in the afternoon, sometimes even later, to make my own breakfast. Afterwards I would go out to see some of my friends in their studios, and at the time most people were thinking of going to bed I sat down to the wonderfully morbid piece of work which I believed was to bring me fame. This was a rather odd book, called " The Fate of Hilary Dale." [1] It has no claim whatever to any immortality, and from my point of view its only value lies in the fact that there is a very brief sketch of Maitland in it. He is described in these words : " Will Curgenven, writer, teacher, and general

[1] *The Degradation of Geoffrey Alwith* (1895).

apostle of culture, as it is understood by the elect, had been hard at work for some hours on an essay on Greek metres, and was growing tired of it. His dingy subject and dingy Baker Street flat began to pall on him, and he rose to pace his narrow room." Now Will Curgenven, of course, was Maitland, and the dingy Baker Street flat was 7 K. " ' Damn the nature of things,' as Porson said when he swallowed embrocation instead of whis-key ! " was what I went on to put into his mouth. This, indeed, was one of Maitland's favourite exclama-tions. It stood with him for all the strange and blas-phemous and eccentric oaths with which I then decorated my language, the result of my experiences in the back-blocks of Australia and on the Pacific Slope of America. In this book I went on to make a little fun of his great joy in Greek metres. I remember that once he turned to me with an assumed air of strange amaze-ment and exclaimed : " Why, my dear fellow, do you know there are actually miserable men who do not know—who have never even heard of—the minuter differences between Dochmiacs and Antispasts ! " That, again, reminds me of a passage in " Paternoster Row," which always gives me acute pleasure because it recalls Maitland so wonderfully. It is where one of the char-acters comes in to the hero and wants his opinion on the scansion of a particular chorus in the " Œdipus Rex." Maydon [1] lays hold of the book, thinks a bit, and begins to read the chorus aloud. Whereupon the other one cries : " Choriambics, eh ? Possible, of course ; but treat them as Ionics a minore with an anacrusis, and see if they don't go better." Now in this passage the speaker is really Maitland, for he involved himself in terms of pedantry with such delight that his eyes gleamed. No doubt it was an absurd

[1] Reardon.

thing, but Greek metres afforded so bright a refuge from the world of literary struggle and pressing financial difficulty.

" Damn the nature of things ! " was Porson's oath. Now Maitland had a very peculiar admiration for Porson. Porson was a Grecian. He loved Greek. That was sufficient for Maitland. In addition to that claim on his love, it is obvious that Porson was a man of a certain Rabelaisian turn of mind, and that again was a sufficient passport to his favour. No doubt if Porson had invited Maitland to his rooms, and had then got wildly drunk, it would have greatly annoyed Maitland ; but the picture of Porson shouting Greek and drinking heavily attracted him immensely. He often quoted all the little stories told of Porson, such as the very well-known one of another scholar calling on him by invitation late one evening, and finding the room in darkness and Porson on the floor. This was when his visitor called out : " Porson, where are the candles, and where's the whiskey ? " and Porson answered, still upon the floor, but neither forgetful of Greek nor of his native wit.

When any man of our acquaintance was alluded to with hostility, or if one animadverted on some popular person who was obviously uneducated, Maitland always vowed that he did not know Greek, and probably or certainly had never starved. His not knowing Greek, was, of course, a very great offence to Maitland, for he used to quote Porson on Hermann :

> " *The Germans in Greek*
> *Are sadly to seek.*
> *Not one in five score,*
> *But ninety-nine more.*
> *All save only Hermann,*
> *And Hermann's a German.*"

Of course a man who lacked Greek, and had not starved, was anathema—not to be considered. And whatever Porson may have done he did know Greek, and that saved his soul. Maitland often quoted with glee what he declared to be some of the most charming lines in the English language :

> " *I went to Strasburg, and there got drunk*
> *With the most learned Professor Brunck.*
> *I went to Wortz, and got more drunken*
> *With the more learned Professor Ruhnken.*"

But if the spirit was willing, the flesh was weak. I never saw Maitland drunk in his life. Indeed he was no real expert in drinking. He had never had any education in the wines he loved. All amateurs of the product of the vine will know how to estimate his actual qualifications as a judge, when I say that Asti, Capri, and especially Chianti seemed to him the greatest wines in the world, since by no means could he obtain the right Falernian of Horace, which, by the way, was probably a most atrocious vintage. As it happened I had been employed for many months on a great vineyard in California, and there had learnt not a little about the making and blending of wine. Added to this I had some natural taste in it, and had read a great deal about wine-making and the great vintages of France and Germany. One could always interest Maitland by telling him something about wine, provided one missed out the scientific side of it. But it was sad that I lacked, from his point of view, the proper enthusiasm for Chianti. Yet, indeed, one knows what was in his classic mind, from the fact that a poor vintage in a real Italian flask, or in something shaped like an amphora, would have made him chuckle with joy far more readily than if a rich man had offered him in a bottle some glorious first growth of the Medoc, Laffite, Latour, or Haut-Brion. But, indeed, he and I, even when I refused indignantly to touch the Italians, and declared with resolution for a wine of Burgundy or the Medoc, rarely got beyond a Bourgeois vintage.

Nevertheless though aspiring to be his tutor in wines I owed him more than is possible to say in the greater matters of education. My debt to him is really very big. It was, naturally enough, through his influence that while still in my one room in Danvers Street I began to read again all the Greek tragedies. By an odd chance I came across a clergyman's son in Chelsea who also had a certain passion for Greek. He used to come to my room and there we re-read the tragedies. My new friend never met Maitland, for Maitland rarely came to my room save on Sundays, and those days were reserved specially for him. But whenever we met, either there or at 7 K, we always read or recited Greek to each other, and then entered into a discussion of the metrical value of the choruses—in which branch of learning I showed proper humility, for in prosody he was remarkably learned. As for me, I knew nothing of it beyond what he told me, and cared very little, personally, for the technical side of poetry. But it was not easy to resist Maitland's enthusiasm, and I succumbed to it so greatly that at last I was really interested in what appealed so to him. Heaven knows, in those days I did at least learn something of the matter.

We talked of rhythm, and of Arsis or Ictus. Pyrrhics we spoke of, and trochees and spondees were familiar on our lips. Especially did he declare that he had a passion for anapæsts, and when it came to actual metres, Choriambics and Galliambics were an infinite joy to him. He explained to me most seriously the

differences between trimeter Iambics when they were
catalectic, acatalectic, hypercatalectic. What he knew
about comic tetrameter was at my service, and in a
short time I knew, as I imagined, almost all that he
did about Minor Ionic, Sapphic, and Alcaic verse.
Once more these things are to me little more than
words, and yet I never hear one of them mentioned—
as one does occasionally when one comes across a
characteristic enthusiast—but I think of Henry Maitland
and his gravely beatific lectures to me on that vastly
important subject. No doubt many people will think
that such little details as these are worth nothing, but
I shall have failed greatly in recording Maitland if they
do not seem something in the end. These trifles are,
after all, touches in the portrait as I see the man, and
that they all meant much to him I know very well.
To get through the early days of literary poverty one
must have ambition and enthusiasm of many kinds.
Enthusiasm alone is nothing, and ambition by itself is
too often barren, but the two together are something
that the gods may fight against in vain. I know that
this association with him, when I was his only friend,
and he was my chief friend, was great for both of us,
for he had much to endure, and I was not without my
troubles. Yet we made fun together of our squalor,
and rejoiced in our poverty, so long as it did not mean
acute suffering ; and when it did mean that, we often
got something out of literature to help us to forget.
On looking back, I know that many things happened
that now seem to me dreadful, but then they appeared
but part of the day's work.

It rarely happened that I went to him without
some story of the week's events, to be told again in
return something which had occurred to him. For
instance, there was that story of the lady who asked

him his experience with regard to the management of butlers. In return I could tell him of going out to dinner at houses where people would have been horrified to learn that I had eaten nothing that day, and possibly nothing the day before. For us to consort with the comfortably situated sometimes seemed to both of us an intolerably fine jest, which was intensified by the difference of these comfortable people from the others we knew. Here and there we came across some fatly rich person who, by accident, had once been deprived of his usual dinner. It seemed to give him a sympathetic feeling for the very poor. But, after all, though I did sometimes associate with such people, I was happier in my own room with Maitland, or in his flat, where we discussed our Æschylus, or wrought upon metres or figures of speech—always a great joy to us. Upon these, too, Maitland was really quite learned. He was full of examples of brachylogy. Anacoluthon he was well acquainted with. Not even Farrar, in his " Greek Syntax," or some greater man, knew more examples of chiasmus, asyndeton, or hendiadys. In these byways he generally rejoiced, and we were never satisfied unless at each meeting, wherever it might be, we discovered some new phrase, or new word, or new quotation.

Once at 7 K I quoted to him from Keats' " Endymion " [1] the lines about those people who " unpen their baaing vanities to browse away the comfortable green and juicy hay from human pastures." All that evening he was denouncing various comfortable people who fed their baaing vanity on everything delightful. He declared they browsed away all that makes life worth while, and in return for my gift to him of this noble quotation he produced something rather more

[1] Book III, ll. 2–5.

H.M.—6

astounding, and perhaps not quite so quotable, out of Zola's " Nana." We had been talking of realism, and of speaking the truth, of being direct, of not being mealy-mouthed ; in fact, of not letting loose " baaing vanities," and suddenly he took down " Nana " and said, " Here Zola has put a phrase in her mouth which rejoices me exceedingly. It is a plain, straightforward, absolutely characteristic sentiment, such as we in England are not allowed to reproduce. Nana, on being remonstrated with by her lover-in-chief for her infidelities, returns him the plain and direct reply, ' Quand je vois un homme qui me plaît, je couche avec.' " He went on to declare that writing any novels in England was indeed a very sickening business, but he added, " I really think we begin to get some-what better in this. However, up to the last few years, it has been practically impossible to write anything more abnormal about a man's relations with women than a mere bigamy." Things have certainly altered, but he was himself one of those who helped to break down that undue sense of the value of current morality which has done so much harm to the study of life in general, and indeed to life itself. His general rage and quarrel with that current morality, for which he had not only a contempt, but a loathing which often made him speechless, comes out well in what he thought and expressed about the Harold Frederick [1] affair. There was, as everybody knows, a second illegitimate family. While the good and orthodox made an effort to help the wife and the legal children, they did their very best to ignore the second family. However, to Maitland's great satisfaction, there were certain people, notably Mrs. Stephens, who did their very best for the other children and for the poor mother. Maitland himself

[1] Harold Frederic (1856–98).

subscribed, before he knew the actual position, to both families, and betrayed extraordinary rage when he learnt how that second family had been treated, and heard of the endeavours of the " unco' guid " to pretend they did not exist.  But such actions and such hypocrisy are characteristic of the middle class in this country, and not in this country alone.  He loathed their morals which become a system of cruelty ;  their greed and its concomitant selfishness :  their timidity which grows brutal in defence of a position to which only chance and their rapacity have entitled them.

Apropos of his hatred of accepted morality, it is a curious thing that the only quarrel I ever had with him showed his early point of view rather oddly. Among the few men he knew there was one, with whom I was a little acquainted, who had picked up a young girl in a tavern and taken her to live with him.  My own acquaintance with her led to some jealousy between me and the man who was keeping her, and he wrote to Maitland complaining of me, and telling him many things which were certainly untrue.  Maitland, having ruined his own life for ever and ever by his relations with a woman of this order, had naturally built up a kind of theory of these things as a justification for himself.  This may seem a piece of extravagant psychology, but I have not the least doubt that it is true. Without asking my view of the affair he wrote to me angrily, and declared that I had behaved badly.  He added that he wished me to understand that he considered an affair of that description as sacred as any marriage.  Though he was young, and in these matters no little of a prig, I was also young, and of a hot temper. That he had not made any inquiries of me, or even asked my version of the circumstances, so angered me that I wrote back to him saying that if he spoke to me in that way I should decline to have anything more to do with him. As he was convinced, most unjustly, that his view was entirely sound, this naturally enough led to an estrangement which lasted for the best part of a year, but I am glad to remember that I myself made it up by writing to him about one of his books. This was before I went to America. It was a grief to me that we did not meet during this estrangement for any of our great talks, which, both then and afterwards, were part of my life, and no little part of it. Often when I think of him I recollect those lines of Callimachus to Heraclitus in Cory's " Ionica " :

" *They told me, Heraclitus, they told me you were dead,*
  *They brought me bitter news to hear and bitter tears to shed.*
  *I wept, as I remembered, how often you and I*
  *Had tired the sun with talking and sent him down the sky.*"

# IV

IN the last chapter I quoted from Boswell, always a favourite of Maitland's, as he is of all true men of letters. But there is yet another quotation from the same work which might stand as a motto for this book, as it might for the final and authoritative biography of Maitland which will perhaps some day be written : " He asked me whether he had mentioned, in any of the papers of the ' Rambler,' the description in Virgil of the entrance into Hell, with an application to the Press ; ' for,' said he, ' I do not much remember them.' I told him, ' No.' Upon which he repeated it :

> ' *Vestibulum ante ipsum primisque in faucibus Orci,*
> *Luctus et ultrices posuere cubilia Curæ ;*
> *Pallentesque habitant Morbi, tristisque Senectus,*
> *Et Metus, et malesuada Fames, ac turpis Egestas ;*
> *Terribiles visu formæ : Letumque, Labosque.*'[1]

' Now,' said he, ' almost all these apply exactly to an author ; all these are the concomitants of a printing-house.' " [2] Nevertheless, although cares, and sometimes sullen sorrows, want, and fear, still dwelt with Maitland, a little time now began for him in which he had some peace of mind, if not happiness. That was a plant he never cultivated. One of his favourite

---

[1] *Æneid*, VI, 273-77.
[2] *Tour to the Hebrides*, under October 14, 1773 ; in a footnote to which the passage of Virgil is given in Dryden's translation, thus :

> *Just in the gate, and in the jaws of hell,*
> *Revengeful cares, and sullen sorrows dwell ;*
> *And pale diseases, and repining age ;*
> *Want, fear, and famine's unresisted rage ;*
> *Here toils and death, and death's half-brother, sleep,*
> *Forms terrible to view, their sentry keep.*

passages from Charlotte Brontë, whose work was in many ways a passion to him, is that in which she exclaims : " Cultivate happiness ! Happiness is not a potato," and indeed he never grew it. Still there were two periods in his life in which he had some peace, and the first period now began. I speak of the time after the death of his first wife. The drain of ten shillings a week—which must seem so absurdly little to many—had been far more than he could stand, and many times he had gone without the merest necessities of life so that the poor alien in the New Cut should have money, even though he knew that she spent it at once upon drink and forgetfulness. Ten shillings a week was very much to him. For one thing it might mean a little more food and better food. It meant following up his one great hobby of buying books. Those who know " The Meditations," know what he thought of books, for in that respect this record is a true guide, even if it should be read in most respects with caution. Yet although he was happier and easier, it is curious that his most unhappy and despairing books were written during this particular period. " In the Morning," [1] it is true, was done before his wife died, and some people who do not know the inner history of the book may not regard it as a tragedy. In one sense, however, it was one of the greatest literary tragedies of Henry Maitland's life, according to his own statement to me.

At that time he was publishing books with the firm of Miller and Company,[2] and knew John Glass,[3] who read for them. It seems that Glass, who had naturally enough, considering his period, certain old-fashioned ideas on the subject of books and their endings, absolutely and flatly declined to recommend his firm to

---

[1] *A Life's Morning* (1888).    [2] Smith, Elder & Co.    [3] James Payn (1830–98).

publish " In the Morning," unless Maitland re-wrote
the natural tragic end of the book and made it turn out
happily. I think nothing on earth, or in some hell for
men of letters, could have made Maitland more angry
and wretched. If there was one thing that he clung to
during the whole of his working time, it was sincerity,
and sincerity in literary work implies an absolute freedom from alien and extrinsic influence. I can well
remember what he said to me about Glass' suggestion.
He abused him and the publishers ; the public, England,
the world, and the very universe. He almost burst
into tears as he explained to me what he had been
obliged to do for the sake of the great fifty pounds he
was to get for the book. For at this time he only got
fifty pounds for a long three-volume novel. He always
wrote with the greatest pain and labour, but I do not
suppose he ever put anything on paper in his life which
cost him such acute mental suffering as the last three
chapters which were written to John Glass' barbaric
order.

After his wife's death he wrote " The Under-World," [1]
" Bond and Free," [2] " Paternoster Row," and " The
Exile." It is a curious fact, although it was not always
obvious even to himself, and is not now to anybody
but me, that I stood as a model to him in many of
these books, especially, if I remember rightly, for one
particular character in " Bond and Free." Some of
these sketches are fairly complimentary, and many are
much the reverse. The reason of this use of me was
that till much later he knew very few men intimately
but myself ; and when he wanted anybody in his
books of a more or less robust character, and sometimes
more or less of a kind that he did not like, I, perforce,
had to stand for him. [3] He owned this to me, and once

---

[1] *The Nether World* (1889). [2] *The Emancipated* (1890). [3] See *Introduction* p. 14.

he was not at all sure how I should take it. As a matter of fact the most life-like portrait of me ends as a villain, and, as he had touched me off to the very life in the first volume, it did make me feel a little sorer than I acknowledged. I leave the curious to discover this particular scoundrel. It was only natural that my wild habits and customs, the relics of Australia and America, afforded him amusement and matter for study. On one occasion they cost him, temporarily, the very large sum of three pounds. As he said, he used to look upon me as a kind of hybrid, a very ridiculous wild man with strong literary leanings, with an enormous amount of general and unrelated knowledge and, at the same time, as a totally unregulated or ill-regulated ruffian. This was a favourite epithet of his, for which I daresay there was something to be said. Now one Sunday it happened that I was going up to see him at 7 K, and came from Chelsea with two or three books in my hand, and a pair of spectacles on my nose. I carried an umbrella, and no doubt looked exceedingly peaceful. As a result of this a young man, who turned out afterwards to be a professional cricketer, thought I was a very easy person to deal with, and to insult. As I came to York Place, which was then almost empty of passers-by, I was walking close to the railings and this fellow came up and, pushing past rudely, stepped right in front of me. Now this was a most outrageous proceeding, because he had fifteen free feet of pavement, and I naturally resented it. So making a little longer step than I should otherwise have done I " galled his kibe." He turned round upon me, and using very bad language, asked me where I was going, who I thought I was, and what I proposed to do about it. I did not propose to do anything, but did it. I smote him very hard with the umbrella, knocking him down. He remained on the pavement for a considerable time, and then only got up at the third endeavour, and promptly gave me into custody. The policeman, who had happened to see the whole affair, explained to me, with that civility common among the custodians of order to those classes whose dress suggests they are their masters, that he was compelled to take the charge. I was removed to Lower Seymour Street and put in a cell for male prisoners only, where I remained fully half an hour.

While I was in this cell a small boy of about nine was introduced and left there. I went over to him and said, " Hullo, my son, what's brought you here ? " Naturally enough he imagined that I was not a prisoner but a powerful official, and bursting into tears he said, " Oh, please, sir, it warn't me as nicked the steak ! " I consoled him to the best of my ability until I was shortly afterwards invited down to Marlborough Street Police Court, where Mr. De Rutzen, later Sir Albert De Rutzen, was sitting. As I had anticipated the likelihood of being fined, and had no more than a few shillings with me, I had written a letter to Maitland, and procuring a messenger through the police, had sent it up to him. He came down promptly and sat in the court while I was being tried for this assault. After hearing the case Mr. De Rutzen decided to fine me three pounds, which Maitland paid, with great chuckles at the incident, even though he considered his prospect of getting the money back for some months was exceedingly vague. It was by no means the first time that he had gone to the police court for copy, which " is very pretty to observe," as Pepys said, when after the Fire of London it was discovered that as many churches as public houses were left standing in the city. That such a man should have had to pursue his studies of actual life in the police courts and the slums was really an outrage, another example of the native malignity of matter. For, as I have insisted, and must again insist, he was a scholar and a dreamer. But his pressing anxieties for ever forbade him to dream, or to pursue scholarship without interruption. He desired time to perfect his control of the English tongue, and he wanted much that no man can ever get. It is my firm conviction that if he had possessed the smallest means he would never have thought himself completely master of the medium in which he worked. He often spoke of poor Flaubert saying : " What an accursed language is French ! " He was for ever dissatisfied with his work, as an artist should be, and I think he attained seldom, if ever, the rare joy that an artist has in accomplishment. It was not only his desire for infinite perfection as a writer pure and simple that afflicted him. It was the fact that he should never have written fiction at all. He often destroyed the first third of a book. I know he did so with one three times over. This, of course, was not always the result of the cool persuasion that what he had done was not good, for it often was good in its way, but frequently he began, in a hurry, in despair, and with the prospect of starvation, something that he knew not to be his own true work, or something that he forced without adequate preparation. Then I used to get a dark note saying, " I have destroyed the whole of the first volume and am, I hope, beginning to see my way." It was no pleasant thing to be a helpless spectator of these struggles, in which he found no rest, when I knew his true destiny was to have been a scholar at a great university.

When one understands his character, or even begins to understand it, it is easy enough to comprehend that the temporary ease with regard to money which came after his wife's death did not last very long. The pressure of her immediate needs and incessant demands being at last relaxed, he relaxed his efforts in certain directions and was presently again in difficulties. It will seem very extraordinary to all but those who know the inside of literary life that this should have been so. A certain amount of publicity is almost always associated in the minds of the public with monetary success of a kind. Yet one very well-known acquaintance of mine, an eminent if erratic journalist, one day had a column of favourable criticism in a big daily, and after reading it went out and bought a red herring with his last penny and cooked it over the fire in his solitary room. It was the same with myself. It was almost the same with Maitland even at this time. No doubt the worst of his financial difficulties were before I returned from America, certainly they were before his wife died, but never, till the end of his life, was he at ease with regard to money. He could not attain the art of the pot-boiler by which most of us survive, even when he tried short stories, which he did finally after I had for some years pressed him to attempt them.

In many ways writing to him was a kind of sacred mission. It was not that he had any faith in great results to come from it, but the profession of a writer was itself sacred, and even the poorest sincere writer was a *sacer vates*. He once absolutely walked all the way to Chelsea to show me a well-known article in which Robert Louis Stevenson denied, to my mind not unjustly, that a writer could claim payment at all, seeing that he left the world's work to do what he chose to do for his own pleasure. Stevenson went on to compare such a writer to a *fille de joie*. This enraged Maitland furiously. I should have been grieved if he

and Stevenson had met upon that occasion. I really
think something desperate might have happened, little
as one might expect violence from such a curious
apostle of personal peace as Maitland. Many years
afterwards I related this incident to Robert Louis
Stevenson in Samoa, but I think by that time Maitland
himself was half inclined to agree with his eminent
brother-author. And yet writing was a mission, even
if it was with him an acquired passion ; but his critical
faculties, which were so keenly developed, almost
destroyed him. There can be no stronger proof that
he was not one of those happy beings who take to the
telling of stories because they must, and because it is in
them. There was no time when he was not obliged to
do his best, though every writer knows to his grief that
there are times when the second best must do. And
thus it was that John Glass so enraged him. All those
things which are the care of the true writer were of infinite importance to him. A misprint, a mere " literal,"
gave him lasting pain. He desired classic perfection,
both of work and the mere methods of production. He
would have taken years over a book if fear and hunger
and poverty had permitted him to do so. And yet he
wrote " Isabel," [1] " The Mob," and " In the Morning,"
all in seven months, even while he read through the
whole of Dante's " Divina Commedia " for recreation,
and while he toiled at the alien labour of teaching.
Yet this was he who wrote to one friend : " Would it
not be delightful to give up a year or so to the study of
some old period of English history ? " When he was
thirty-six he said : " The four years from now to forty
I should like to devote to a vigorous apprenticeship in
English." But this was the man who year after year
was compelled to write books which the very essence of

---

[1] *Isabel Clarendon* (1886).

his being told him would work no good. Sometimes I
am tempted to think that the only relief he got for
many, many years came out of the hours we spent in
company, either in his room or in mine. We read very
much together, and it was our delight to exchange
quotations, or read each other passages which we had
discovered during the week. He recited poetry with
very great feeling and skill, and was especially fond of
much of Coleridge. I can hear him now reading those
lines of Coleridge to his son which end :

> " *Therefore all seasons shall be sweet to thee,*
> *Whether the summer clothe the general earth*
> *With greenness, or the redbreast sit and sing*
> *Betwixt the tufts of snow on the bare branch*
> *Of mossy apple-tree, while the nigh thatch*
> *Smokes in the sun-thaw ; whether the eave-drops fall*
> *Heard only in the trances of the blast,*
> *Or if the secret ministry of frost*
> *Shall hang them up in silent icicles,*
> *Quietly shining to the quiet Moon.*"

And to hear him chant the mighty verse of the great
Greeks who were dead, and yet were most alive to
him, was always inspiring. The time was to come,
though not yet, when he was to visit Greece, and when
he had entered Piræus and seen the peopled mountains
of that country Homer became something more to him
than he had been, while the language of Æschylus and
Sophocles took on new glories and clothed itself in still
more wondrous emotions. He knew by heart a hundred
choruses of the Greek tragedies, and declaimed them
with his wild hair flung back and his eyes gleaming as
if the old tragedians, standing in the glowing sun of the
Grecian summer, were there to hear him, an alien yet
not an alien, using the tongue that gave its chiefest

glories to them for ever. But he had been born in exile, and had made himself an outcast.

Those who have read so far, and are interested in him, will see that I am much more concerned to say what I felt about him than to relate mere facts and dates. I care little or nothing that in some ways others know more or less of him, or know it differently. I try to build up my little model of him, try to paint my picture touch by touch ; often, it may be, by repetition, for so a man builds himself for his friends in his life. I must paint him as a whole, and put him down, here and there perhaps with the grain of the canvas showing through the paint, or perhaps with what the worthy critics call a rich impasto, which may be compiled of words. Others may criticise, and will criticise, what I write. No doubt they will find much of it wrong, or wrong-headed, and will attribute to me other motives than those which move me, but if it leads them to bring out more of his character than I know or remember, I shall be content. For the more that is known of him, the more he will be loved.

It was somewhere about this time that I undertook to write one of two or three articles which I have done about him for periodicals, and the remembrance of that particular piece of work reminds me strongly of his own ideas of his own humour in writing. There have been many discussions, wise and otherwise, as to whether he possessed any at all, and I think the general feeling that he was very greatly lacking in this essential part of the equipment of a writer to be on the whole true. Among my lost letters there was one which I especially regret not to be able to quote, for it was very long, containing perhaps two thousand words, which he sent to me when he knew I had been asked to do this article. Now the purport of Maitland's letter was to prove that every one was wrong who said he had no humour. In one sense there can be no greater proof that anybody who said so was right. He enumerated carefully all the characters in all the books he had hitherto written in whom he thought there was real humour. He gave me a preposterous list of these individuals, with his comments, and appealed to me in all deadly seriousness to know whether I did not agree with him that they were humorous. But the truth is that, save as a talker, he had very little humour, and even then it was frequently verbal. It was, however, occasionally very grim, and its strength, oddly enough, was of the American kind, since it consisted of managed exaggeration. He had a certain joy in constructing more or less humorous nicknames for people. Sometimes these were good, and sometimes bad, but when he once christened them he kept to it always. I believe the only man of his acquaintance who had no nickname was George Meredith, but then he loved and admired Meredith in no common fashion.

In some of his books he speaks, apparently not without some learning, of music, but there are, I fancy, signs that his knowledge of it was more careful construction than actual knowledge or deep feeling. Still, he did at times discover a real comprehension of the greater musicians, especially of Chopin. Seeing that this was so, it is very curious, and more than curious in a writer, that he had a measureless adoration of barrel organs. He delighted in them strangely, and when any Italian musician came into his dingy street or neighbourhood, he would set the window open and listen with ardour. Being so poor, he could rarely afford to give away money even in the smallest sum. Pennies were indeed pennies to him. But he did sometimes bestow pence on wandering Italians who ground out Verdi in the crowded streets. Among the many languages he knew was, of course, Italian ; for, as I have said, he read the " Divina Commedia " easily, reading it for relaxation as he did Aristophanes. It was a great pleasure to him, even before he went to Italy, to speak a few words in their own tongue to these Italians of the English streets. He remembered that this music came from the south, the south that was always his Mecca, the Kibleh of the universe. Years afterwards, when he was in the south, and knew Naples and the moving crowds of the Chiaia—long before I had been there and had listened to its uproar from the Belvedere of San Martino—he found Naples chiefly a city of this simple popular music. Naples, he said, was the most interesting modern city in Europe ; and yet I believe the chief pleasure he had there was hearing its music, and the singing of the lazzaroni down by Santa Lucia. " Funiculi, Funicula," he loved as much as if it were the work of a classic, and " Santa Lucia " appealed to him like a Greek chorus. I remember that, years later, he wrote to me a letter of absurd and exaggerated anger, which was yet perfectly serious, about the action of the Neapolitan municipality in forbidding street organs to play in the city. Sometimes, though rarely, seeing that he could not often afford a shilling, he went to great concerts in London. He spoke in " The Vortex " as one not without instruction in musical subjects, but I fancy that musical experts might find flaws in his technical knowledge. Nevertheless he did love music with passion.

He was a man not without a certain sensuality, but it was his sensuousness which was in many ways the most salient point in his character. As I often told him, he was a kind of incomplete Rabelaisian. That was suggested to me by his delighted use of Gargantuan epithets with regard to the great recurrent subject of food. He loved all things which were redolent of oil and grease and fatness. The joy of abundance appealed to him, and I verily believe that to him the outstanding characteristic of the past in England was its abundant table.[1] Indeed, in all things but rowdy indecency, he was a Rabelaisian, and being such, he yet had to put up with poor and simple food. However, provided it was at hand in large quantities, he was ready to feed joyously. He would exclaim : " Now for our squalid meal ! I wonder what Harold Edgeworth, or good old Edmund Roden would say to this ? " When I think of the meagre preface that Harold Edgeworth wrote in later years for " Basil," when that done by G. H. Rivers [2]—afterwards published separately—did not meet with the approval of Maitland's relatives and executors, I feel that Edgeworth somewhat deserved the implied scorn of Maitland's words. As for Edmund Roden, he often spoke of him affectionately. In later years he sometimes went down to Felixstowe to visit him. He liked his house, and was much at home in it. It was there that he met Grant Allen, and Sir Luke Redburn,[3] whom he declared to be the most interesting people he saw in Felixstowe at that time.

I am not sure whether it was on this particular occasion, perhaps in 1895,[4] that he went to Essex with a great prejudice against Grant Allen.[5] The reason of

[1] One of his old school-fellows says of the brassy-voiced individual spoken of in *The Meditations*, " I knew the latter well, our drill instructor, a ' Professor ' St. Ruth. . . . As regards his fondness for abundance of food his nick-name at school was ' Trough.' I remember him deeply interested in some Greek or Latin book—twisting his handkerchief and biting his nails—he would suddenly laugh loudly at something that had taken his fancy. He never joined in any games, although from his build you would have thought he would have made a good forward at Rugby." (*R.*)
[2] H. G. Wells (1866–1946).
[3] Probably Sir Benjamin Ward Richardson, physician (1828–96).
[4] June 1895.
[5] For Gissing on Grant Allen, see *Henry Ryecroft :* " Autumn," IX.

H.M.—7

this was curious. He was always most vicious when any writer, who obviously lived in comfort, complained loudly and bitterly of the meagre support given him by the public, and the public's faithful servants, the publishers. When Allen growled furiously on this subject in a newspaper interview Maitland recalled to me with angry amusement a certain previous article in which, if I remember rightly, Grant Allen proclaimed his absolute inability to write if he were not in a comfortable room with rose-coloured curtains. " Rose-coloured curtains ! " said Maitland contemptuously, and looking round his own room one certainly found nothing of *that* kind. It was an extraordinary thing, one of the many odd things in his character, that the man who loved the south so, who always dreamed of it, seemed to see everything at that period of his life in the merest black and white. There was not a spark or speck of colour in his rooms. Now in my one poor room in Chelsea I had hung up all sorts of water-colours acquired by various means from artists who were friends of mine. By hook or by crook I got hold of curtains with colour in them, and carpets, too, and Japanese fans. My room was red and yellow and scarlet, while his were all a dingy monochrome, as if they sympathised with the outlook at the back of his flat, which stared down upon the inferno of the Metropolitan Railway. But to return to Grant Allen. Maitland now wrote : " However, I like him very much. He is quite a simple and very gentle fellow, crammed with multifarious knowledge, enthusiastic in scientific pursuits. With fiction and that kind of thing he ought never to have meddled ; it is the merest pot-boiling. He reads nothing whatever but books of scientific interest."

It was at Felixstowe, too, that he met Carew Latter [1]

---

[1] Clement Shorter (1857–1926).

who induced him to write twenty papers in one of the
journals Latter conducted. They were to be of more or
less disreputable London life. Some of them have been
reprinted in his volumes of short stories. There is
certainly no colour in them ; in some ways they resemble sketches with the dry-point. After he had once
been on the Continent, and had got south to Marseilles
and the Cannebière, he learnt to know what colour
was, and wrote of it in a way he had never done before,
as may be noticed particularly in one paragraph about
Capri seen at sunset from Naples. In this sudden
discovery of colour he reminded me, oddly enough, of
my old acquaintance Wynne, the now justly celebrated
painter, who, up to a certain time in his life, had
painted almost in monochrome, and certainly in a perpetual grey chord. Then he met Marvell, the painter,
who was above all things a colourist. I do not think
Marvell influenced Wynne in anything else, but from
that day Wynne was a colourist, and so remains,
although to it he has added a great and real power of
design and decoration. It is true that Maitland never
became a colourist in writing, but those who have read
his work with attention will observe that after a certain
date he was much more conscious of this prismatic
world.

In those days our poverty and our ambition made
great subjects for our talks. I had myself been writing
for some years with no more than a *succès d'estime*, and
sometimes thought that I would throw up the profession
and go back to Australia or America, or to the sea, or
would try Africa at last. But Maitland had no such
possibilities within him. He maintained grimly, though
not without humour, that his only possible refuge when
war, or some other final disaster made it impossible for
writers to earn their difficult living, was a certain block

of buildings opposite 7 K. This, however, was not Madame Tussaud's as the careless might imagine, but the Marylebone workhouse, which he said he regarded with a proprietary eye. It always afforded him a subject for conversation when his prospects seemed rather poorer than usual. It was, he declared, very handy for him when he became unable to do more work. No doubt this was his humour, but there was something in this talk which was more than half serious. He always liked to speak of the gloomy side of things, and I possess many letters of his which end with references to the workhouse, or to some impending, black disaster. In one he said : " I wish I could come up, but am too low in health and spirits to move at present. A cold clings about me, and the future looks dark." Again he said : " No, I shall never speak of my work. It has become a weariness and toil—nothing more." And again : " It is a bad, bad business, that of life at present." And yet once more : " It is idle to talk about occupation—by now I have entered on the last stage of life's journey." This was by no means when he had come towards the end of his life. However, the workhouse does recur, even at the end, in a letter written about two months before his death. He wrote to me : " I have been turning the pages with great pleasure, to keep my thoughts from the workhouse." Those who did not know him would not credit him with the courage of desperation which he really possessed, if they saw his letters and knew nothing more of the man.

# V

THE art of portraiture, whether in words or paint, is very difficult, and appears even less easy as I attempt to draw Maitland. Nevertheless the time comes when the artist seems to see his man standing on his feet before him, put down in his main planes, though not yet, perhaps, with any subtlety. The anatomy is suggested at any rate, if there are bones in the subject or in the painter. As it seems to me, Maitland should now stand before those who have read so far with sympathy and understanding. I have not finished my drawing, but it might even now suffice as a sketch and seem from some points of view to be not wholly inadequate. It is by no means easy to put him down in a few words, but patience and the addition of detail reach their end, it may be not without satisfaction—for " with bread and steel one gets to China." It is not possible to etch Maitland in a few lines, for as it seems to me it is the little things in his character with which I am most concerned that give him his greatest value. It is not so much the details of his actual life, but what he said, and the way he seemed to think, or even the way he avoided thinking, which I desire to put down. And when I say those things he wished not to think of, I am referring more especially to his views of the universe, and of the world itself, those views which are a man's philosophy, and not less his philosophy when of set purpose he declines to think of them at all, for this Maitland did without any doubt. Goethe said, when he spoke, if I remember rightly, about all forms of religious and metaphysical speculation,

" Much contemplation, or brooding over these things is disturbing to the spirit." Unfortunately I do not know German, so I cannot find the reference to this, but Maitland, who knew the language very thoroughly and had read nearly everything of importance in it, often quoted this passage, having naturally a great admiration for Goethe. I do not mean that he admired him merely for his position in the world of letters. What he admired in Goethe was what he himself liked and desired so much. He wished for peace, for calmness of spirit. He did not like to be disturbed in any way. He would not disturb himself. He asked people to be reasonable, and thought this was a reasonable request to make of them. I remember on one occasion when I had been listening to him declaiming about some one's peculiar lack of reasonableness, which seemed to him the one great human quality, that I said : " Maitland, what would you do if you were having trouble with a woman who was in a very great rage with you ? " He replied, with an air of surprise, " Why, of course, I should reason with her." I said shortly, " Don't ever get married again ! " Nevertheless he was a wonderfully patient and reasonable man himself, and truly lacked everything characteristic of the combatant. He would discuss, he would never really argue. I do not suppose that he was physically a coward, but a dread of scenes and physical violence lay very deep in his organisation. Although he used me as a model I never really drew him at length in any of my own books, but naturally he was a subject of great psychological interest to me. Pursuing my study of him I said, one day, " Maitland, what would you do if a man disagreed with you, got outrageously and unreasonably angry, and slapped you in the face ? " He replied, in his characteristically low and concentrated voice, " Do ? I should look at him with the most infinite disgust, and turn away."

His horror of militarism was something almost comic, for it showed his entire incapacity for grasping the world's situation as it shows itself to any real and ruthless student of political sociology who is not bogged in the mud flats of some Utopian island. Once we were together on the Horse Guards' Parade and a company of the Guards came marching by. We stood to watch them pass, and when they had gone he turned to me and said, " Mark you, my dear man, this, *this* is the nineteenth century ! " In one of his letters written to me after his second marriage he said of his eldest son : " I hope to send him abroad, to some country where there is no possibility of his having to butcher or be butchered." [1] This, of course, was pure reason pushed to the point where reason becomes mere folly, for such is the practical antinomy of pure reason in life.

It was in this that he showed his futile idealism, which was in conflict with his real pessimism. That he did good work in many of his books dealing with the lower classes is quite obvious, and cannot be denied. He showed us the things that exist. It is perfectly possible, and even certainly true, that many of the most pessimistic writers are in reality optimists. They show us the grey in order that we may presently make it rose. But Maitland wrote absolutely without hope. He took his subjects as mere subjects, and putting them on the table, lectured on pathology. He made books of his dead-house experiences, and sold them, but never believed that he, or any other man, could really do good by speaking of what he had seen and dilated upon. The people as a body were vile and hopeless. He did not even inquire how they became so. He thought

[1] This boy was killed in France in 1915 or 1916. (*R.*)

nothing could be done, and did not desire to do anything. His future was in the past. The world's great
age would never renew itself, and only he and a few
others really understood the desperate state into which
things had drifted. Since his death there has been some
talk about his religion. I shall speak of this later, on a
more fitting occasion ; but, truly speaking, he had no
religion. When he gave up his temporary Positivist
pose, which was entirely due to his gratitude to Harold
Edgeworth for helping him, he refused to think of these
things again. They disturbed the spirit. If I ever
endeavoured to inveigle him into a discussion or an
argument upon any metaphysical subject he grew
visibly uneasy. He declined to argue, or even to discuss, and though in later life he admitted that immortality was perhaps possible, I defy any one to bring a
tittle of evidence to show that he ever went further.
This attitude to all forms of religious and metaphysical
thought was very curious to me. It was, indeed,
almost inexplicable, as I have an extreme pleasure in
speculative inquiry of all kinds. The truth is that
on this side of his nature he was absolutely wanting.
Such things interested him no more than music interests
a tone-deaf man who cannot distinguish the shriek of a
tom-cat from the sound of a violin. If I did try to
speak of such things he listened with an air of outraged
and sublime patience which must have been obvious to
any one but a bore. Whether his philosophy was sad
or not, he would not have it disturbed.

His one interest in religion seemed to lie in his notion
that it was a curious form of delusion almost ineradic-
able from the human mind. There is a theory, very
popular among votaries of the creeds, which takes the
form of denying that any one can really be an atheist.
This is certainly not true, but it helps us to understand

the theological mind, which has an imperative desire to lay hold of something like an inclusive hypothesis to rest on. So far as Maitland was concerned there was no more necessity to have a hypothesis about God than there was to have one about quaternions, and quaternions certainly did not interest him. He shrugged his shoulders and put these matters aside, for in many things he had none of the weaknesses of humanity, though in others he had more than his share. In his letters to Rivers, there are a few references to Rivers' habits of speculation. I think it was somewhere in 1900 or 1901 that he read " Forecasts." [1] By this time he had a feeling of affection for Rivers, and some admiration for him. His references to him in " The Meditations " [2] are sufficiently near the truth to corroborate this. Nevertheless his chief feeling towards Rivers and his work, beyond the mere fact that it was a joy to him that a man could make money by doing good stuff, was one of amazement that any one could be deeply interested in the future, and could give himself almost wholly or even with partial energy, to civic purposes. And so he wrote to Rivers : " I must not pretend to care very much about the future of the human race. Come what may, folly and misery are sure to be the prevalent features of life, but your ingenuity in speculation, the breadth of your views, and the vigour of your writing, make this book vastly enjoyable. The critical part of it satisfies, and often delights me. Stupidity should have a sore back for some time to come, and many a wind-bag will be uneasily aware of collapse."

It is interesting to note, now that I am speaking of his friendship for Rivers, and apropos of what I shall

[1] *Anticipations* (1901).
[2] *Henry Ryecroft :* " Summer," XXIII, where Wells figures as N——.

have to say later about his religious views, that he wrote to Rivers : " By the bye, you speak of God. Well, I understand what you mean, but the word makes me stumble rather. I have grown to shrink utterly from the use of such terms, and though I admit, perforce, a universal law, I am so estranged by its unintelligibility that not even a desire to be reverent can make those old names in any way real to me." So later he said that he was at a loss to grasp what Rivers meant when he wrote : " There stirs something within us now that can never die again." I think Maitland misinterpreted the passage, which was rather apropos of the awakening of the civic spirit in mankind than of anything else, but he went on to say that he put aside the vulgar interpretation of such words. However, was it Rivers' opinion that the material doom of the earth did not involve the doom of earthly life ? He added that Rivers' declared belief in the coherency and purpose of things was pleasant to him, for he himself could not doubt for a moment that there *was* some purpose. This is as far as he ever went. On the other hand, he did doubt whether we, in any sense of the pronoun, should ever be granted understanding of that purpose. All this shows that he possessed no metaphysical endowments or apparatus. He loved knowledge pure and simple, but when it came to the exercises of the metaphysical mind he was pained and puzzled. He lacked any real education in philosophy, and did not even understand its peculiar vocabulary. However vain those of us who have gone through the metaphysical mill may think it in actual products, we are all aware that it helps greatly to formulate our own philosophy, or even our own want of it. For it clears the air. It cuts away all kinds of undergrowth. It at any rate shows us that there is no metaphysical way out, for the simple reason that there has never existed one metaphysician who did not destroy another. They are all mutually destructive. But Maitland had no joy in construction or destruction ; and, as I have said, he barely understood the technical terms of metaphysics. There was a great difference with regard to these inquiries between him and Rivers. The difference was that Rivers enjoyed metaphysical thinking and speculation while Maitland hated it. But Rivers took it up much too late in life, and about the year 1900 made wonderful discoveries which had been commonplaces to Aristotle. This would not have mattered much if he had regarded it as education. However, he regarded it as discovery, and wrote books which inspired debates, and apparently filled the metaphysicians with great joy. It is always a pleasure to the ironic spirit to see clever people show that they are not equally clever in every direction.

It is curious how this native dislike of Maitland to being disturbed by speculative thought comes out in a criticism he made of Thomas Hardy. He had always been one of this writer's greatest admirers, and I know he especially loved " The Woodlanders," but he wrote in a letter to Dr. Lake something very odd about " Jude the Obscure." He calls it : " a sad book ! Poor Thomas is utterly on the wrong tack, and I fear he will never get back into the right one. At his age, a habit of railing at the universe is not overcome." This criticism is wholly without any value as regards Hardy's work, but it is no little side-light on Maitland's own peculiar habits of thought, or of persistent want of thought, on the great matters of speculation. His objection was not to anything that Hardy said, but to the fact that the latter's work, filled with what Maitland calls " railing at the universe," personally disturbed him. Anything which broke up his little semi-classic universe, the literary hut which he had built for himself as a shelter from the pitiless storm of cosmic influences, made him angry and uneasy for days and weeks. He never lived to read Hardy's " Dynasts," a book that stands almost alone in literature, and is to my mind a far greater book than Goethe's " Faust," but if he had read it I doubt if he would have forgiven Thomas Hardy. He always wanted to be left alone. He had constructed his pattern of the universe, and any one who shook it he denounced with, " Confound the fellow ! He makes me unhappy." The one book that he did read, which is essentially a disturbing book to many people, and apparently read with some pleasure, was the earliest volume of Frazer's " Golden Bough " ; but it is noteworthy that what interested him, and indeed actually pleased him, was Frazer's side attacks upon the dogmas of Christianity. He said : " The curious thing about Frazer's book is, that in illustrating the old religious usages connected with tree-worship and so on, he throws light upon every dogma of Christianity. This by implication ; he never does it expressly. Edmund Roden has just pointed this out to the Folk-lore Society, with the odd result that Gladstone wrote at once resigning membership." This was written after Gladstone died, but it reads as if Maitland was not aware that he was dead. Odd as it may seem, it is perfectly possible that he did not know it. He cared very little for the newspapers, and sometimes did not read any for long periods. It is rather amusing that when I proved to him in later years that he had once dated his letters according to the Positivist Calendar, he seemed a little disturbed and shocked. Still, it was very natural that when exposed to Positivist influences he should have become a Positivist, for among the people of that odd faith, if faith it can be called, he found both kindness and intellectual recognition. When his mind became clearer and calmer, and something of the storm and stress had passed by, he was aware that his attitude had been somewhat pathologic, and did not like to recall it. This became very much clearer to him, and indeed to me, when another friend of ours, a learned and very odd German who lived and starved in London, went completely under in the same morbidly religious way. His name was Schmidt.[1] He remained to the day of Maitland's death a very great friend of his, and I believe he possesses more letters from Henry Maitland than any man living—greatly owing to his own vast Teutonic energy and industry in writing to his friends.

In London Schmidt came to absolute destitution. It then appeared that he owned a collie dog, which he found at last impossible to feed, even though he starved himself to do so. Maitland told me of this, and introduced me to Schmidt. On hearing his story, and seeing the dog, I went to my own people, who were living in Clapham, and asked them if they would take the animal from Schmidt and keep it. When I saw the German again I was given the dog, together with a paper on which were written all Don's peculiar tricks, most of which had been taught him by his master and needed the German language for their words of command. Soon after this Schmidt fell into even grimmer poverty, and was rescued from the deepest gulf by some religious body analogous in those days to the Salvation Army of the present time. Of this Maitland knew nothing, until on going down the Strand he found his friend giving away religious pamphlets at the door of Exeter Hall. When he told me this he said he went

[1] Eduard Bertz. For Gissing on Bertz, see *Henry Ryecroft :* " Autumn," VII.

next day to see the man in his single room lodging and found him sitting at the table with several open Bibles spread out before him. He explained that he was making a commentary on the Bible at the instigation of one of his new friends, and he added : " Here, *here*, is henceforth my life's work." Shortly after this, I believe through Harold Edgeworth or some one else to whom Maitland appealed, the poor German was given work in some quasi-public institution, and with better fare and more ease his brain recovered. He never mentioned religion again. It was thus that Maitland himself recovered from similar but less serious influences in somewhat similar conditions. For some weeks in 1885 I was myself exposed to such influences in San Francisco, in even bitterer circumstances than those from which Schmidt and Maitland had suffered, but not for one moment did I alter my opinions. As a kind of final commentary on this chapter and this side of Maitland's mind, one might quote from a letter to Rivers : " Seeing that mankind cannot have done altogether with the miserable mystery of life, undoubtedly it behoves us before all else to lighten as we best can the lot of those for whose being we are responsible. This for the vast majority of men—a few there are, I think, who are justified in quite neglecting that view of life, and, by the bye, Marcus Aurelius was one of them. Nothing he could have done would have made Commodus other than he was—I use, of course, the everyday phrases, regardless of determinism —and then one feels pretty sure that Commodus was not his son at all. For him, life was the individual, and whether he has had any true influence or not, I hold him absolutely justified in thinking as he did." There again comes out Maitland's view, his anti-social view, the native egoism of the man, his peculiar solitude of thought.

# VI

TO have seen " Shelley plain " once only is to put down a single point on clear paper. To have seen him twice gives his biographer the right to draw a line. Out of three points may come a triangle. Out of the many times in many years that I saw Maitland comes the intricate pattern of him. I would rather write a little book like " Manon Lescaut " than many biographical quartos lying as heavy on the dead as Vanbrugh's mansions. If there are warts on Maitland so there were on Cromwell. I do not invent like the old cartographers, who adorned their maps with legends saying, " Here is much gold," or " Here are found diamonds." Nor have I put any imaginary " Mountains of the Moon " into his map, or adorned vacant parts of ocean with whales or wonderful monsters. I put down nothing unseen, or not most reasonably inferred. In spite of my desire to say little about myself, it is necessary to speak sometimes of things primarily my own. There is no doubt it did Maitland a great deal of good to have somebody to interest himself in, even if it were one of no more importance than myself. Although he was so singularly a lonely man, he could not always bury himself in the classics, or even in his work, done laboriously in eight prodigious hours. We talked for ever about what we were going to do, and there was very little that I wrote, up to the time of his leaving London permanently, which was not discussed with him. Yet I knew that he was wholly dissatisfied with much I wrote. When I was still living in Chelsea, he came to me one Sunday in a very uneasy state of mind. He looked obviously worried, and was for a long time silent as he sat over the fire. I asked him again and again what was the matter, because, as can be easily imagined, I always had the notion that something must be the matter with him, or soon would be. In answer to my repeated importunities he said, at last : " Well, the fact of the matter is, I want to speak to you about your work." It appeared that my affairs were at the bottom of his discomfort. He told me that he had been thinking of my want of success, and that he had made up his mind to tell me the cause of it. He was nervous and miserable, though I begged him to speak freely, but at last got out the truth. He told me that he did not think I possessed the qualities to succeed at the business I had so rashly commenced. He declared that it was not that he had not the very highest opinion of such a book as " The Western Trail," but as regards my story-writing he felt it was bound to be a failure. Those who knew him can imagine what it cost him to say as much as this. He would have preferred to destroy half a book and begin it again. Naturally enough I found what he said very disturbing, but am pleased to say that I took it in good part, and told him that I would think it over seriously. As may be imagined, I did a great deal of thinking on the subject, but the result of my cogitations amounted to this : I had started a thing and meant to go through with it at all costs. I wrote so to him later, and the little incident never made any difference whatever to our affectionate friendship. When I come to speak of some of his letters about my later books it will be seen how generous he could be to a friend who, for some time then, had not been very enthusiastic about his own work. I always believed that it was he and not myself who was at the wrong kind of task. Fiction,

even as he understood it, was not for a man of his
nature and faculties. He would have been in his true
element as a don of a college, and much of his love of
the classics was a mystery to me, as it would have been
to most active men of the world, however well educated.
I did understand his passion for the Greek tragedies,
but he had almost more delight in the Romans ; and,
with the exception of Catullus and Lucretius, the Latin
classics are to me without much savour. There is
no doubt that in many ways I was but a barbarian to
him. For one thing, at that time I was something of a
fanatical imperialist. He took no more interest in the
Empire, except as literary material, than he did in
Nonconformist theology. Then I was certainly highly
patriotic as regards England, but he was very cosmo-
politan. It was no doubt very strange that he should
have spoken to me about my having little faculty for
writing fiction when I had so often come to the same
silent conclusion about himself. I did not dare to tell
him so, for if such a pronouncement had distressed me
a little it would distress him very much more. Yet I
think he did sometimes understand his real limitations,
especially in later years, when he wrote more criticism.
The man who could say that he was prepared to spend
his years from thirty-six to forty in a vigorous apprenticeship to English, was perfectly capable of continuing that
apprenticeship until he died.

He took a critical and wonderful interest in the
methods of all men of letters, and that particular
interest with regard to Balzac, which was known to
many, has sometimes been mistaken. Folks have said,
and even written, that he meant to write an English
" Comédie Humaine." There is, no doubt, a touch of
truth in this notion, but no more than a touch. He
would have liked to follow in Balzac's mighty footsteps,

and do something for England which would possibly be inclusive of all social grades. At any rate he began at the bottom and worked upwards. It is quite obvious to me that what prevented him from going further in any such scheme was not actually a want of power or any failure of industry ; it was a real lack of knowledge and of close contact with the classes composing the whole nation. Beyond the lower middle class his knowledge was not very deep. He was mentally an alien, and a satiric if interested intruder. He had been exiled for the unpardonable sins of his youth. It is impossible for any man of intellect not to suspect his own limitations, and I am sure he knew that he should have been a pure child of books, for as soon as he got beyond the pale of his own grim surroundings, those surroundings which had been burnt, and were still being burnt into his soul, he apparently lost interest. Though two or three of these later books have indeed much merit, such novels as " The Vortex " and " The Best of All Things " [1] are really failures. I believe he felt they were. Anthony Hope Hawkins once wrote to me apropos of something, that there were very few men writing who really knew that all real knowledge had to be " bought." Maitland had bought his knowledge of sorrow and suffering and certain surroundings at a personal price that few can pay and not be bankrupt. But while I was associating with almost every class in the world he lived truly alone. There were, indeed, long months when he actually saw no one, and there were other periods when his only friend besides myself was that philosophic German whose philosophy put its lofty tail between its legs on a prolonged starvation diet.

As one goes on talking of him and considering his nature there are times when it seems amazing that he

[1] *The Crown of Life* (1899).

did not commit suicide and have done with it. Certainly there were days and seasons when I thought this might be his possible end. But some men break and others bend, and in him there was undoubtedly some curious strength though it were but the Will to Live of Schopenhauer, the one philosopher he sometimes read. I used myself to think that it was perhaps his native sensuousness which kept him alive in spite of all his misery. No man ever lived who enjoyed more acutely than himself things that were even remotely enjoyable, though his general attitude towards life was like his attitude towards people and the world. For so many good men Jehovah would have spared the Cities of the Plains. So in a certain sense the few good folk that he perceived in any given class made him endure the others that he hated, while he painted those he loved against their dingy and dreadful background. The motto on the original title page of " The Under-World " was a quotation from a speech by Renan delivered at the Académie Française in 1889 : " La peinture d'un fumier peut être justifiée pourvu qu'il y pousse une belle fleur ; sans cela, le fumier n'est que repoussant." The few beautiful flowers of the world for Henry Maitland were those who hated their surroundings and desired vainly to grow out of them. Such he pitied, hopeless though he believed their position, and vain though he knew their aspirations to be. In a way all this was nothing but translated self-pity. Had he been more fortunate in his youth I do not believe he would have ever turned his attention in any way towards social affairs, in which he took no native interest. His natural sympathy was only for those whom he could imagine to be his mental fellows. Almost every sympathetic character in all his best books was for him like the starling in the cage of Sterne—the starling that

cried, " I can't get out ! I can't get out ! " Among
the subjects he refused to speak of or to discuss was one
that for a long time greatly interested me, and interests
me still—I refer to Socialism. But then Socialism,
after all, is nothing but a more or less definitive view
of a definite organisation with perfectly recognised
ends, and he saw no possibility of any organisation
doing away with the things he loathed. That is to
say, he was truly hopeless, most truly pessimistic. He
was a sensuous and not a scientific thinker, and to get
on with him for any length of time it was necessary to
suppress three-quarters of the things I wished to speak
about. He was a strange egoist, though truly the
hateful world was not his own. It appeared to me that
he prayed, or strove, for the power to ignore it. It is
for this reason that it seems to me now that all his so-
called social work and analysis were in the nature of an
alien *tour de force*. He bent his intellect in that direction,
and succeeded even against his nature. He who desired
to be a Bentley or a Porson wrote bitterly about the
slums of Tottenham Court Road. With Porson he
damned the nature of things, and wrote beautifully
about them. I remember on one occasion telling him
of a piece of script in the handwriting of the great
surgeon, John Hunter, which ran somewhat like this :
" Damn civilisation ! It makes cats eat their kittens,
sows eat their young, and women send their children
out to nurse." I think that gave him more appreciation
of science than anything he had ever heard. For it
looked back into the past, and for Henry Maitland the
past was the age of gold. In life, as he had to live it,
it was impossible to ignore the horrors of the present
time. He found it easier to ignore the horrors of the
past, and out of ancient history he made his great
romance, which, truly, he never wrote.

It is odd that a man who was thus so essentially romantic should have been mistaken, not without good reason, for a realist. In one sense he was a realist, but this was the fatal result of his nature and his circumstances. Had he lived in happier surroundings, still writing fiction, it would have been romance. And yet, curiously enough, I doubt if any of his ideas concerning women were at all romantic. His disaster with his first wife was due to early and unhappily awakened sex feeling, but I think he believed that his marrying her was due to his desire to save somebody, whom he considered to be naturally a beautiful character, from the dunghill on which he found her. This poor girl was his first *belle fleur*. In all his relations with women it seems as if his own personal loneliness was the dominating factor. So much did he feel these things that it was rarely possible to discuss them with him. Nevertheless it was the one subject, scientifically treated, on which I could get him to listen. In the first five years of my literary apprenticeship I began a book, which is still unfinished, and never will be finished, called " Social Pathology." [1] So far as it dealt with sex and sex deprivation, he was much interested in it. In all his books there is to be found the misery of the man who lives alone and yet cannot live alone. I do not think that in any book but " The Unchosen " [2] he ever made a study of that from the woman's side. But it is curiously characteristic of his sex view that the chief feminine character of that book apparently knew not love even when she thought that she knew it, but was only aware of awakened senses.

One might have imagined, considering his early experiences, that he would have led the ordinary life of man, and associated, if only occasionally, with women

[1] Possibly *Bio-Politics* (1938).     [2] *The Odd Women* (1893).

of the mercenary type. This, I am wholly convinced, was a thing he never did, though I possess one poem which implies the possible occurrence of such a passing *liaison*. There was, however, another incident in his life which occurred not long before I went to America. He was then living in one room in the house of a journey-man bookbinder. On several occasions when I visited him there I saw his landlady, a young and not un-pleasing woman, who seemed to take great interest in him, and did her very best to make him comfortable in narrow, almost impossible, surroundings. Her husband, a man a great deal older than herself, drank, and not infrequently ill-treated her. This was not wholly Maitland's story, for I saw the man myself, as well as his wife. It seems that she went for sympathy to her lodger, and he told her something of his own troubles. Their common griefs threw them together. She had obviously more than the usual intelligence of her class. She desired to learn French, or made Maitland believe so ; my own view being that she desired his company. The result of this was only natural, and soon afterwards Maitland was obliged to leave the house owing to the jealousy of her husband, who for many years had already been suspicious of her without any cause. But this was only a passing affair. He took other rooms, and so far as I know never saw her again.

While I was in America he was living at 7 K, and in that gloomy flat there was an affair of another order, an incident not without many parallels in the lives of poor artists and writers. It seems that a certain lady, not without importance in society, and the wife of a rich husband, wrote to him about one of his books, and having got into correspondence with him allowed her curiosity to overcome her discretion. She visited him often in his chambers, and though he told me but little

I gathered what the result was. So far as I am aware these were the only two romantic or quasi-romantic incidents in Maitland's life until towards the end of it. When I came back from America he certainly had no mistress, and beyond an occasional visit from the sons of Harold Edgeworth, he received no one but myself. His poverty forbade him entertaining any but one of his fellows who was as poor as he was, and the few acquaintances he had once met in better surroundings than his own gradually drifted away from him, or died as Cotter Morison died. Although he spoke very little about these matters of personal loneliness and depriva-tion I was yet conscious, from the general tenor of his writing and an occasional dropped word, how bitterly he felt them. It had rejoiced my unregenerate heart in America to learn that he was not entirely without feminine companionship at a time when the horror of his life was only partially mitigated by the preference of his mad and wretched wife for the dens and slums of the New Cut. This woman of the upper classes came to him like a star, and had been a lamp in his darkness. I wonder if she still retains within her heart some memories of those hours.

I have not been able to discover whether some of Maitland's ancestors were German. He thought this was so, without having anything definite to go upon. If it were true perhaps his Teutonic ancestry made him turn with joy to the German ideal of woman, that of the haus-frau. If little or nothing were known about him, or only so much as those know who have already written of him, it might, in some ways, be possible to reconstruct him by a process of deductive analysis, by what the school logicians call the *regressus a principiatis ad principia*. This is always a fascinating mental exercise, and indeed, with a very little light on Maitland's career, it should not have been difficult for some to build up a picture not unlike the man. For instance, no one with a gleam of intelligence, whether a critic or not, could read some portions of the chapter in " Victorian Novelists " [1] on " Women and Dickens " without coming to the inevitable conclusion that Maitland's fortune with regard to the women with whom he had been thrown in contact must have been disastrous. Although Dickens drew certain offensive women with almost unequalled power, he treats them so that one becomes oblivious of their very offensiveness, as Maitland points out. Maitland's own commentary on such women is ten thousand times more bitter, and it is *felt*, not observed, as in Dickens' books. He calls them " these remarkable creatures," and declares they belong mostly to one rank of life, the lower middle class. " In general their circumstances are comfortable . . . nothing is asked of them but a quiet and amiable discharge of their household duties ; they are treated by their male kindred with great, often with extraordinary consideration. Yet their characteristic is acidity of temper and boundless licence of querulous or insulting talk. The real business of their lives is to make all about them as uncomfortable as they can. Invariably, they are unintelligent and untaught ; very often they are flagrantly imbecile. Their very virtues (if such persons can be said to have any) become a scourge. In the highways and byways of life, by the fireside, and in the bed-chamber, their voices shrill upon the terrified ear." He adds that no historical investigation is needed to ascertain the truthfulness of these presentments. Indeed Maitland required no historical investigation, he had his personal experience to go upon ; this, indeed, is obvious. Still, one cannot

[1] *Charles Dickens : a Critical Study* (1898).

but feel, in reading this indictment, that something might be said upon the other side, and that Maitland's attitude was so essentially male as to vitiate many of his conclusions.

A few pages further on in this book he says : " Another man, obtaining his release from these depths, would have turned away in loathing ; Dickens found therein matter for his mirth, material for his art." But Maitland knew that Dickens had not suffered in the way he himself had done. Thus it was that he rejoiced in the punishment which Mrs. Joe Gargery received. Maitland writes : " Mrs. Joe Gargery shall be brought to quietness ; but how ? By a half-murderous blow on the back of her head, from which she will never recover. Dickens understood by this time that there is no other efficacious way with these ornaments of their sex."

Having spoken of Dickens it may be as well to dispose of him, with regard to Maitland, in this chapter. It seems to be commonly thought that Maitland wrote his book about the Victorian novelists not only with the sympathy which he expressed, but with considerable joy in the actual work. This is not true, for he regarded it essentially as a pot-boiler, and did it purely for money. By some strange kink in his mind he chose to do it in Italy, far from any reference library. He wrote : " My little novelist book has to be written before Christmas, and to do this I must get settled at the earliest possible date in a quiet north Italian town. I think I shall choose Siena." On what principle he decided to choose a quiet north Italian town to write a book about Victorian novelists I have never been able to determine, as he had no overwhelming love of North Italy, which was for him the Italy of the Renaissance. Indeed, he actually disliked the work, and had no desire to do it, well as it was done. It is, however, curious, to me, in considering this book, to find that neither he nor any other critic of Dickens that I have ever read seems to give a satisfactory explanation of the great, and at times overwhelming, attraction that Dickens has for many. And yet on more than one occasion I discussed Dickens with him, and in a great measure he agreed with a theory I put forth with some confidence. The great charm of Dickens lies not wholly in his humour or even greatly in his humour. It is not found in his characterisation, nor in his underlying philosophy of revolt, although almost every writer of consequence is a revolutionist. It results purely and simply from what the critics of the allied art of painting describe as " quality." This is a word exceedingly difficult to define. It implies more or less the characteristic way in which paint is put upon the canvas. A picture may be practically worthless from the point of view of subject or composition, it may even be comparatively poor in colouring, and yet it may have an extreme interest or surface. One finds the same thing in Dickens' writings. His page is full. It is fuller than the page of any other English writer. There are, so to speak, on any given page by any man a certain number of intellectual and emotional stimuli. Dickens' page is full of these stimuli to a most extreme degree. It is like a small mosaic, and yet clear. It has cross meanings, cross lights, reflections, suggestions. Compare a page of Dickens with a page, say, of Thackeray. Take a pencil and write down the number of mental suggestions given by a sentence of Thackeray. Take, again, a sentence of Dickens, and see how many more there are to be found. It is this tremendous and overflowing fullness which really constitutes Dickens' great and peculiar power.

But all this is anticipation. Not yet was he to write of Dickens, Thackeray, and the Brontës, for much was to befall him before he went to Italy again. He was once more alone, and it might have been prophesied that this loneliness would not last long. I have often regretted not foreseeing what might have been foreseen if I had considered the man and his circumstances with the same fullness which comes to one in later years after Fate has wrought itself out. Had I known all that might have been known, or done all that might have been done, I could perhaps have saved him from something even worse than his first marriage. Yet, after all, I was a poor and busy man, and while living in Chelsea had many companions, some of them men who have now made a great name in the world of art. The very nature of Maitland and his work, the dreadful concentration he required to do something which was, as I insist again, alien from his true nature, forbade my seeing him very often, or even often enough to gather from his reticence what was really in his mind. Had I visited him without any warning, it would have utterly destroyed his whole day's work. But this solitude, this enforced and appalling loneliness, which seemed to him necessary for work if he was to live, ate into him deeply. It destroyed his nerve and what judgment he ever had which, heaven knows, was little enough. What it means to some men to live in such solitude only those who know can tell, and they never tell. To Maitland, with his sensual and sensuous nature, it was most utter damnation.

By now he had come out of the pit of his first marriage, and gradually the horrors he had passed through became dim to his eyes. They were like a badly toned photograph, and faded. I did foresee that something would happen sooner or later to alter the way in which he

lived, but I did not foresee, and could not have foreseen
or imagined what was actually coming, for no one could
have prophesied it. It was absurd, impossible, monstrous, and almost bathos. Yet it fits in with the
character of the man as it had been distorted by circumstance. One Sunday when I visited him he told
me, with a strange mixture of abruptness and hesitation,
that he had made the acquaintance of a girl in the
Marylebone Road. Naturally enough I thought at
first that his resolution and his habits had broken down
and that he had picked up some prostitute of the
neighbourhood. But it turned out that the girl was
" respectable." He said : " I could stand it no longer,
so I rushed out and spoke to the very first woman I
came across." It was an unhappy inspiration of the
desperate, and the first act in a prolonged drama of
pain and misery. It took me some time and many
questions to find out what this meant, and what it was
to lead to, but presently he replied sullenly that he
proposed to marry the girl if she would marry him.
On hearing this, I fell into silence, and we sat for a
long time without speaking. Knowing him as I did, it
was yet a great shock to me. For I would rather have
seen him in the physical clutches of the biggest harpy
in the Strand—knowing that such now could not long
hold him. I had done my best, as a mere boy, to
prevent him from marrying his first wife, and had failed
with the most disastrous results. I now determined to
stop this marriage if possible and ventured to recall the
past and the part I had played in it when I implored
him to have no more to do with Marian Hilton long
before he married her. I reminded him of the relief it
had been when his first wife died, but nothing that I
could say seemed to move, or even to offend him. His
mind recognised its truth, but his body meant to have

its way. He was quiet, sullen, set—even when I told him that he would repent it most bitterly. The only thing I could at last get him to agree to was that he would take no irrevocable step for a week.

I asked him questions about the girl. He admitted that he did not love her in any sense of the word love. He admitted that she had no great powers of attraction, that she seemed to possess no particularly obvious intellect. She had received his advances in the street in the way that such girls, whose courtship is traditionally carried on in the open thoroughfare, do receive them. But when he asked her to visit him in his chambers she replied to that invitation with all the obvious suspicion of a lower-class girl from whom no sex secrets were hidden. From the very start the whole affair seemed hopeless, preposterous, intolerable, and I went away from him in despair. It was a strange thing that Maitland did not seem to know what love was. If I have not before this said something about his essential lack of real passion in his dealings with women it must be said now. It is quite obvious that he had a boyish kind of passion for Marian Hilton, but it was certainly not that kind of passion which mostly keeps boys innocent. Indeed those calf loves which afflict youths are at the same time a great help to them, for a boy is as naturally coy as any maiden. If by any chance Maitland, instead of coming into the hands of a poor little harlot of the streets of Moorhampton, had fallen in love with some young girl of decent character and upbringing, his passions would not have been so fatally roused. I think it was probably the whole root of his disaster that this should have occurred at all. Possibly it was the horror and rage and anger connected with the first affair, combined with the fact that it became actually sensual, which prevented him from having afterwards what one might without priggishness describe as a pure passion. At any rate I never saw any signs of his being capable of the overwhelming love which might in other circumstances drive a man down to hell, or raise him to heaven. To my mind all his books betray an extreme lack of this. His characters in all their love-affairs are essentially too reasonable. A man wishes to marry a girl, not because he desires her simply and overwhelmingly, but because she is a fitting person, or the kind of woman about whom he has been able to build up certain ideas which suit his mind. In fact the love of George Hardy [1] for Isabel [2] in " The Exile " is somewhat typical of the whole attitude he had towards affairs of passion. Then again in " Paternoster Row " there is the suicide of Gifford [3] which throws a very curious light on Maitland's nature. Apparently Gifford did not commit suicide because of his failure, or because he was half starving, but because he was weakly desirous of a woman like Anne [4]—not necessarily Anne herself. In Maitland's phrase, he desired her to complete his manhood, to my mind the most ridiculous way of putting the affair. It is in this that Maitland showed his essential lack of knowledge of the other sex. A man does not captivate women by going to them and explaining, with more or less periphrasis, that they are required to complete his manhood, that he feels a rather frustrate male individual without them. And if he has these ideas at the back of his head and goes courting, the result is hardly likely to be successful. Maitland never understood the passion in the man that sweeps a woman off her feet. One finds this lack in all his men who live celibate lives. They suffer physically, or they suffer to a certain degree from

---

[1] Godwin Peak.  [2] Sidwell Warricombe.
[3] Harold Biffen.  [4] Amy Reardon.

loneliness, but one never feels that only one woman
could cure their pain, or alleviate their desolation. At
times Maitland seemed, as it were, to be in love with
the sex but not with the woman. Of course he had a
bitter hatred of the general prejudices of morality, a
thing which was only natural to any one who had lived
his life and thought what he thought. It is pleasing to
note that his favourite poem in the whole English
language was perhaps the least likely one that could be
picked out. This was Browning's " Statue and the
Bust," which is certainly of a teaching not Puritan in
its essence. The Puritan ideal Maitland loathed with
a fervour which produced the nearest I have ever seen
in him to actual rage and madness. He roared against
it if he did not scoff. He sometimes quoted the well-
known lines from the almost unknown Brathwaite :

> " *Where I saw a Puritane-one*
> *Hanging of his Cat on Monday,*
> *For killing of a Mouse on Sonday.*"

I remember very well his taking down Browning when
I was with him one afternoon at 7 K. He read aloud a
great portion of " The Statue and the Bust," and we
discussed it afterwards, of course pointing out to each
other with emphasis its actual doctrine, its loathing of
futility. It teaches that the two people who loved each
other but never achieved love were two weaklings, who
ought to have acted, and should not have allowed
themselves to be conquered by the lordly husband.
Maitland said : " Those people who buy Browning
and think they understand him—oh, if they really
knew what he meant they would pick him up with a
pair of tongs, and take him out, and burn him in their
back yards—in their back yards ! " It strikes one that
Maitland, in his haste, seemed to think that the kind

of bourgeois or bourgeoise, whom he imagined thus destroying poor Browning with the aid of tongs, possessed such things as back-yards, and, perhaps, frequented them on Sunday afternoons. But he had lived for so many years in houses which had not a garden, or anything but a small, damp yard behind, that he began to think, possibly, that all houses were alike. I roared with laughter at his notion of what these prosperous Puritans would do. It suggested to my mind a picture of some well-dressed woman of the upper middle-class bringing out " The Statue and the Bust " with a pair of tongs, and burning it in some small and horrible back-yard belonging to a house in the slums between Tottenham Court Road and Fitzroy Square. And yet, although he understood Browning's sermon against the passive futility of these weak and unfortunate lovers he could not, I think, have understood wholly, or in anything but a literary sense, the enormous power of passion which Browning possessed a knowledge of. This lack in him is one of the keys to his character, and it unlocks much. When I left him after he told me about this new affair, I went back to my own rooms and sat thinking it over, wondering if it were possible even now to do anything to save him from his own nature, and the catastrophe it was preparing. Without having seen the girl I felt sure that it would be a catastrophe, for I knew him too well. On reflecting over the matter it did seem to me that there was one possible chance of saving him from himself. It was a very unlikely thing that I should succeed, but at any rate one plan might be tried.

I have said that we rarely spoke of his early life, and never of what had happened in Moorhampton. Nevertheless I was fully aware that it dominated the whole of his outlook and all his thoughts in any way connected with ordinary social life, especially with regard to intercourse with those who might know something about his early career. At this time I do not think that he actually blamed himself much for what had happened. Self-esteem has great powers of repair. Men die many times in life and are born again, and by this time he must have looked on the errant youth who had been himself as little more than an ancestor. He himself had died and risen again, and if he was not the man he might have been, he was certainly not the man he had been. Yet he was perpetually alive to what other people might possibly think of him. The real reason for his almost rigid seclusion from society was his very natural fear that some brute, and he knew only too well that there are such brutes, might suddenly and unexpectedly expose his ancient history. It is true that even in our society in England, which is not famous all the world over for tact, it was not very likely to happen. But the bare possibility that it might absolutely dominated him. It requires very little sympathy or understanding of his character to see that this must have been so. No doubt it was mainly from this cause that he considered he had no right to approach women of his own class, seeing that he had declassed himself, without telling the whole truth. But this was quite impossible for him to do, and I knew it. In some cases it would have been wise, in some unwise, but Henry Maitland was unable to do such a thing. The result was this sudden revolt, and the madness which led him to speak to this girl of the Marylebone Road, whom I pictured, not inadequately, in my mind. At the first glance it seemed that nothing could possibly be done, that the man must be left to " dree his weird," to work out his fate and accomplish his destiny. And yet I lay awake for a very long time that night thinking of the whole

H.M.—9

situation, and at last determined to take a step on his behalf which, at any rate, had the merit of some originality and courage.

Years ago in Moorhampton, when he was a boy, before the great disaster came, Maitland had visited my uncle's house, and had obviously pleased every one he met there. He was bright, not bad looking, very cheerful and enthusiastic, and few who met him did not like him. Among those whose acquaintance he made at that house were two of my own cousins. In later years they often spoke of him to me, even although they had not seen him since he was a boy of seventeen. I now went to both of them and told them the whole affair in confidence, speaking quite openly of his character, and the impossibility he discovered within himself of living in the desolation which fate had brought upon him. They understood his character, and were acquainted with his reputation. He was a man of genius, if not a man of great genius, and occupied a certain position in literature which would one day, we all felt assured, be still a greater position. They were obviously exceedingly sorry for him, and not the less sorry when I told them of the straits in which he sometimes found himself. Nevertheless it seemed to me, as I explained to them, that if he had been lucky enough to marry some one in sympathy with him and his work, some one able to help to push him forward on the lines on which he might have attained success, there was yet great hope for him even as regards money. Then I asked them whether it would not be possible to stop this proposed outrageous marriage, which seemed to me utterly unnatural. They were, however, unable to make any suggestion, and certainly did not follow what was in my mind. Then I opened what I had to say, and asked them abruptly if it were not possible for one of them to consider whether she would marry him if the present affair could be brought decently to an end. They were both educated women, and knew at least two foreign languages. They were accustomed to books, and appreciated his work.

No doubt my proposal sounded absurd, unconventional, and perhaps not a little horrifying. But when I have had anything to do in life I have not been accustomed to let convention stand in my way. Such marriages have been arranged and have not been unsuccessful. There was a real possibility of such a marriage as I proposed being anything but a failure. Our conversation ended at last in both of them undertaking to consider the matter if, after meeting Maitland again, they still remained of the same mind, and if he found that such a step was possible. I have often wondered since whether any situation exactly like this ever occurred before. I found it very interesting, and when at last I went back to Maitland I felt entitled to tell him that he could do much better than marry an unknown girl of the lower classes whom he had accosted in desperation. But he received what I had to say in a very curious manner. It seemed to depress him profoundly. Naturally enough, I did not tell him the names of those who were prepared to renew his acquaintance, but I did tell him that I had been to a lady who had once met him and greatly admired his work, who would be ready to consider the possibility of becoming his wife if on meeting once again they proved sympathetic. He shook his head grimly, and, after a long silence, told me that he had not kept his word, and had asked Ada Brent [1] to marry him. He had, he said, gone too far to withdraw.

There is such a thing in life as the tyranny of honour,

[1] Edith Underwood (m. 1891).

and personally I cared very little for this point of honour when I thought of his future. It was not as if this girl's affections were in any way engaged. If they had been I would have kept silence, bitterly as I regretted the whole affair. She was curious about him, and that was all. It would do her no harm to lose him, and, indeed, as the event proved, it would have been better if she had not married at all. Therefore I begged him to shut up the flat and leave London at once, even offering to try and find the money for him to do so. But, like all weak people, he was peculiarly obstinate, and nothing that could be urged had the least effect upon him. I have often thought it was his one great failure in rectitude which occurred at Moorhampton that made him infinitely more tenacious of doing nothing which might seem in any way dishonourable, however remotely. I did not succeed in moving him, with whatever arguments I plied him, and the only satisfaction I got out of it was the sense that he knew I was most deeply interested in him, and had done everything, even much more than might have been expected, to save him from what I thought must lead to irreparable misery. Certainly the whole incident was remarkable. There was, perhaps, a little air of curiously polite comedy about it, and yet it was the prelude to a tragedy.

It was soon after this, in fact it was on the following Sunday, that I made the acquaintance of the young woman who was to be his second wife, to bear his children, to torture him for years, to drive him almost mad, and once more make a financial slave of him. We three met in the gloomy sitting-room of 7 K. My first impression of this girl was more unfavourable than I had expected. She was the daughter of a small tradesman but little removed from an artisan, and she looked it.  In the marriage certificate her father is described as a carver, for what reason I am unable to determine, for I have a very distinct recollection that Maitland told me he was a bootmaker, probably even a cobbler.  I disliked the young woman at first sight, and never got over my early impression.  From the very beginning it seemed impossible that she could ever become in any remote degree what he might justifiably have asked for in a wife.  Yet she was not wholly disagreeable in appearance.  She was of medium height and somewhat dark.  She had not, however, the least pretence to such beauty as one might hope to find even in a slave of the kitchen.  She possessed neither face nor figure, nor a sweet voice, nor any charm—she was just a female.  And this was she that the most fastidious man I knew was about to marry.  I went away with a sick heart, for it was nothing less than a frightful catastrophe, and I had to stand by and see it happen.  He married her on March 20, 1891,[1] and went to live near Exeter.[2]

[1] This date seems doubtful.  Dr. M. C. Donnelly equally definitely gives February 25, 1891 ; in the parish of St. Pancras.  In any case, Gissing himself had already settled in Exeter by January 20.

[2] From January to August 1891 in rooms at 24 Prospect Park, Exeter ;  and thereafter, until June 1893, in a rented house at 1 St. Leonard's Terrace, Exeter (now demolished).

# VII

FOR many months after he left London I did not see Maitland, although we continued to correspond somewhat irregularly. He was exceedingly reticent about the results of his marriage, and I did not discover definitely for some time to what extent it was likely to prove a failure. In some ways it was a relief to me that he should be living in the country, as I always felt, rightly or wrongly, a certain feeling of responsibility with regard to him when he was close at hand. Marriage always takes one's friends away from one, and for a time he was taken from me. But as I am not anxious to write in great detail about the more sordid facts of his life, especially when they do not throw light on his character, I am not disturbed at knowing little of the earlier days of his second marriage. The results are sufficient, and will presently appear. For Maitland remained Maitland, and his character did not alter now. So I may return for a little while to matters more connected with his literary life.

I have before this endeavoured to describe or suggest his personal appearance, but whenever I think of him I regret deeply that no painter ever made an adequate portrait of the man. He was especially interesting-looking, and most obviously lovable and sympathetic when any of his feelings were roused. His grey eyes were very bright and intelligent, his features finely cut, and at times he was almost beautiful ; although his skin was not always in such a good condition as it should have been, and he was always very badly freckled. For those who have never seen him a photograph published in a dull literary journal, which is now defunct, is

certainly the most adequate and satisfying presentment
of him in existence.[1]  On a close inspection of this
photograph it will be observed that he brushed his hair
straight backward from his forehead without any part-
ing.  He had a curious way of dressing it about which
he was very particular.  It was very fine hair of a
brown colour, perhaps of a rather mousy tint, and it
was never cut except at the ends at the nape of his
neck.  Whenever he washed his face he used to fasten
this hair back with an elastic band which he always
carried in his waistcoat pocket.  On some occasions,
when I have stayed the night at 7 K and seen him at
his toilette, this elastic band gave him a very odd appearance, almost as if he wore, for the time being, a very
odd halo ; but as his hair was so long in front it would
otherwise have fallen into the basin of water.  He told
me that once in Germany a waiter entered the room
while he was washing his face, and on perceiving this
peculiar head-dress betrayed signs of mixed amusement
and alarm.  As Maitland said, " I believe he thought
I was mad."

His forehead was high, his head exceedingly well
shaped but not remarkably large.  He always wore a
moustache.  Considering his very sedentary life his
natural physique was extremely good, and he was
capable of walking great distances if he were put to it
and was in condition.  Seen nude, he had the figure of a
possible athlete.  I used to tell him that he might be
an exceedingly strong man if he cared to take the trouble
to become one, but his belief, which is to be found
expressed in one passage of " The Meditations," was
that no one in our time could be at once intellectually
and physically at his best.  Indeed, he had in a way a
peculiar contempt for mere strength, and I do not doubt

[1] The date of Sir William Rothenstein's drawing of Gissing is June 7, 1897.

that much of his later bodily weakness and illness might have been avoided if he had thought more of exercise and open air.

In no way was he excessive, in spite of his jocular pretence of a monstrous addiction to " strong waters " as he always called them. He did love wine, but he loved it with discretion, although not with real knowledge. It was a case of passion and faith with him. I could imagine that in some previous incarnation—were there such things as reincarnations—he must have been an Italian writer of the South he loved so well. A little while ago I spoke of the strange absence of colour in his rooms. On re-reading " The Meditations," I find some kind of an explanation, or what he considered an explanation, of this fact, to which I myself drew his attention. He seemed to imagine that his early acquaintance with his father's engravings inspired him with a peculiar love of black and white. More probably the actual truth is that his father's possible love of colour had never been developed any more than his own.

His fantastic attempts at times to make one believe that he was a great drinker, when a bottle of poor and common wine served him and me for a dinner and made us cheerful, were no more true than that he was a great smoker. He had a prodigious big pot of tobacco in his rooms in the early days, a pot containing some form of mild returns which to my barbaric taste suggested nothing so much as hay that had been stored next some mild tobacco. It was one of my grievances against him that when I visited his rooms hard up for anything to smoke, which frequently occurred in those days, I was almost unable to use this poor weed. But it was always a form of jest with him to pretend that his habits were monstrously excessive. One of his commonest forms of humour was exaggeration. Many people misunderstood that his very expressions of despair were all touched with a grim humour. Nevertheless he and his rooms were grim enough. On his shelves there was a French book, the title of which I forget, dealing without any reticence with the lives of the band of young French writers under the Second Empire, who perished miserably in the conditions to which they were exposed. This volume contains a series of short and bitter biographies, ending for the most part with, " mourut à l'hôpital," or " se brûla la cervelle." We were by no means for ever cheerful in those times.

I have not said very much, except by bitter implication, of his financial position, or what he earned. But his finances were a part of his general life's tragedy. There is a passage somewhere at the end of a chapter in " In the Morning " which says : " Put money in thy purse ; and again, put money in thy purse ; for, as the world is ordered, to lack current coin is to lack the privileges of humanity, and indigence is the death of the soul." I have been speaking wholly in vain if it is not understood that he was a man extremely difficult to influence, even for his own good. This was because he was weak, and his weakness came out with most exceeding force in all his dealings with publishers and editors. For the most part he was atrociously paid, but the fact remains that he was paid, and his perpetual fear was that his books would presently be refused and that he would get no one to take them, if he remonstrated with those who were his taskmasters. In such an event he gloomily anticipated, not so much the workhouse, but once more a cellar off the Tottenham Court Road, or some low poverty-stricken post as a private tutor or the usher of a poor school. Sometimes when we were together he used to talk with a certain pathetic jocosity, or even jealousy, of Coleridge's luck in having discovered his amiable patron, Gillman.[1] He did not imagine that nowadays any Gillmans were to be looked for, nor do I think that any Gillman would have found Maitland possible. One night after we had been talking about Coleridge and Gillman he sat down and wrote a set of poor enough verses, not without humour, and certainly highly characteristic, that ran as follows :

## THE HUMBLE ASPIRATION OF H. M., NOVELIST

" Hoc erat in votis."

*Oh, could I encounter a Gillman*
*Who would board me and lodge me for aye,*
*With what intellectual skill, man,*
*My life should be frittered away !*

*What visions of study methodic*
*My leisurely hours would beguile !—*
*I would potter with details prosodic,*
*I would ponder perfections of style.*

*I would joke in a vein pessimistic*
*At all the disasters of earth ;*
*I would trifle with schemes socialistic,*
*And turn over matters for mirth.*

*From the quiddities quaint of Quintilian*
*I would flit to the latest critiques ;—*
*I would visit the London Pavilion,*
*And magnify lion-comiques.*

*With the grim ghastly gaze of a Gorgon*
*I would cut Hendersonian bores—*
*I would follow the ambulant organ*
*That jingles at publicans' doors.*

---

[1] Cf. *New Grub Street*, chapter XV.

*In the odorous alleys of Wapping*
*I would saunter on evenings serene ;*
*When the dews of the Sabbath were dropping*
*You would find me on Clerkenwell Green.*

*At the Hall Scientific of Bradlaugh*
*I would revel in atheist rant,*
*Or enjoy an attack on some bad law*
*By the notable Mrs. Besant.*

*I would never omit an oration*
*Of Cunninghame Graham or Burns ;*
*And the Army miscalled of Salvation*
*Should furnish me frolic by turns.*

*Perchance I would muse o'er a mystic ;*
*Perchance I would booze at a bar ;*
*And when in the mind journalistic*
*I would read the " Pall Mall " and the " Star."*

*Never more would I toil with my quill, man,*
*Or plead for the publishers' pay.—*
*Oh, where and Oh, where is the Gillman,*
*Who will lodge me and board me for aye ?*

Now as to his actual earnings. His first book, " Children of the Dawn," was published by Hamerton's.[1] So far as I am aware it brought him in nothing. The book, naturally enough, was a dead failure ; nobody perceived its promise, and it never sold. I do not think he received a penny on account for it. He got little more for " Outside the Pale," [2] which was published in 1884, the year I went to America, and was dedicated to me, as the initials J. C. H.[3] on the dedication page of the first edition testify. At that time I still retained in signature my second initial. This book was published

[1] Remington.
[2] *The Unclassed* (1884).
[3] M. C. R. (*i.e.* Morley Roberts).

by Andrews and Company,[1] and it was through it that he first made acquaintance in a business way with George Meredith, then quite a poor man and working for the firm as a reader.

In " Outside the Pale," as a manuscript there was a chapter, or part of a chapter, of a curiously romantic kind. It was some such theme as that which I myself treated in a romantic story called " The Purification." [2] Hilda Moon,[3] the idealised heroine of the streets, washed herself pure of her sins in the sea at midnight, if I remember the incident rightly, for I never actually read it. It appears that George Meredith was much taken with the story, but found his sense of fitness outraged by the introduction of this highly romantic incident, which seemed out of tone with the remainder of the book and the way in which it was written. He begged Maitland to eliminate it. Now as a rule Maitland, being a young writer, naturally objected to altering anything, but he knew that Meredith was right. At any rate, even at that period, the older man had had such an enormous experience that Maitland accepted his opinion and acted upon it. He told me that George Meredith came downstairs with him into the street, and standing on the doorstep reiterated his advice about this particular passage. He said in the peculiar way so characteristic of him, " My dear sir, I beg you to believe it, it made me *shiver* ! " That passage is missing in the published book.

" Outside the Pale " had a kind of *succès d'estime*. Certain people read it, and fewer people liked it. It was something almost fresh in English. Nevertheless he

---

[1] Bentley ; but there is a confusion here for Roberts really means the firm of Chapman & Hall, for which Meredith was reader. They published Gissing's next novel, *Isabel Clarendon* (1886).

[2] *The Purification of Dolores Silva* (1894).

[3] Ida Starr.

made little or nothing out of it. Few, indeed, were those who made money out of Andrews and Company at that time. The business was run by Harry Andrews,[1] known in the trade as " the liar," a man who notoriously never spoke the truth if a lie would bring him a penny. After " Outside the Pale " came " Isabel," which was obviously written under the influence of Tourgeniev. So far as I am aware this influence has not been noted, even by so acute a critic as Thomas Sackville,[2] but I was at that time a great reader of Tourgeniev, partly owing to Maitland's recommendation and insistence upon the man, and recognised his flavour at once. Maitland openly acknowledged it, a thing no writer does without very strong reason. This book, of course, was not a success. That, I believe, was the last work he published with Andrews and Company. So far as he was concerned the firm had not been a success. He was still compelled to earn his bread and cheese and rent by teaching.

Although Tourgeniev was the earliest great influence upon Maitland, his effect was very largely that of form. So far as feeling was concerned his god for many years was undoubtedly Dostoievsky. That Russian writer himself suffered and had been down into the depths like the modern writer Gorki, which was what appealed to Maitland. Indeed he says somewhere : " Dostoievsky, a poor and suffering man, gives us with immense power his own view of penury and wretchedness." It was Maitland who first introduced " Crime and Punishment " to me. There is no doubt, when one comes to think of it seriously, a great likeness between the modern Russian school and Maitland's work, and that likeness is perhaps founded on something deeper than the mere

[1] Presumably Frederick Chapman. Siegfried Sassoon's *Meredith*, chapter XVI, provides some corroborative detail.
[2] Thomas Seccombe (1866–1923).

community of subject which shows itself here and there. One notes something essentially Slav-like in Maitland's attitude to life. He was a dreamer, rebellious and unable. If, indeed, his ancestry was partly Teutonic, he might have been originally as much Slav as German.

In 1886, while I was still in America, he began " The Mob." At that time, just when he had almost done the first two volumes, there occurred the Trafalgar Square riots, in which John Burns, Hyndman, and Henry Hyde Champion were concerned. Fool though Maitland was about his own affairs, he yet saw that it was a wonderful coincidence from his point of view that at this juncture he should have been dealing with labour matters and the nature of the mob. Some rare inspiration or suggestion led him to rush down with the first two volumes to Messrs. Miller and Company, where they were seen by John Glass, who said to him, " Give us the rest at once and we will begin printing now." He went home and wrote the third volume in a fortnight while the other two volumes were in the press. This book was published anonymously, as it was thought that this would give it a greater chance of success. It might reasonably be attributed to any one, and Maitland's name at that time, or indeed at any time afterwards, was very little help towards financial success. Now I am of opinion, speaking from memory, that this book was bought out and out by the publishing firm for fifty pounds. To a young writer, who had never made so much, fifty pounds was a large sum. In Maitland's exaggerated parlance it was " gross and riotous wealth."

Having succeeded in getting hold of a big firm of notable and well-known publishers, he dreaded leaving them, even though he very soon discovered that fifty pounds for a long three-volume novel was most miserable pay. That he wrote books quickly at times was no guarantee that he would always write them as rapidly. For once in his life he had finished a whole volume in a fortnight, but it might just as well take him many months. There are, indeed, very few of his books of which a great part was not destroyed, re-written, and sometimes again destroyed and again re-written. Nevertheless he discovered a tremendous reluctance to ask for better terms. It was not only his fear of returning to the old irremediable poverty which made him dread leaving a firm which was not all it might have been, but he was cursed with a most unnecessary tenderness for it. He actually dreaded hurting the feelings of a publishing firm which had naturally all the qualities and defects of a corporation. The reason that he did at last leave it was rather curious. It shows that what many might think a mere coincidence may prejudice a fair man's mind.

As I have said, he had been in the habit of selling his books outright for fifty pounds. After this had gone on for many books I suggested to him, as everything he wrote went into several editions under the skilful management of the firm, that it might be as well to sell them the first edition only and ask for a royalty on the succeeding ones. This would never have occurred to him, and he owned it was a good idea. So when " The Flower " [1] was finished he sold the first edition for forty pounds, and arranged for a percentage on succeeding editions. He went on with the next book at once. Now as it happened, curiously enough, there was no second edition of " The Flower " called for, and this so disheartened poor Maitland that he sold his two next novels outright for the usual sum.

One day when I was with him he spoke of the bad luck of " The Flower," which seemed to him almost

---

[1] *Thyrza* (1887).

inexplicable. It was so very unlucky that it had not done well, for the loss of the extra ten pounds was not easy for him to get over in his perpetual and grinding poverty. When we had discussed the matter he determined to ask the firm what they would give him for all further rights in the book. He did this, and they were kind enough to pay the sum of ten pounds for them, thus making up the old price of fifty pounds for the whole book. Then, by one of those chances which only business men are capable of thoroughly appreciating, a demand suddenly sprang up for the story, and the publishers were enabled to bring out a new edition at once. Some time later it went into a third edition, and, I believe, even into a fourth. Now it will hardly be credited that Maitland was very sore about this, for he was usually a very just man, but when I suggested, for the hundredth time but now at the psychological moment, that the firm of Bent and Butler [1] who were then publishing for me, might give him very good terms, he actually had the courage to leave his own publishers, and never went back to them.

I have insisted again and again upon Maitland's weakness and his inability to move. Nothing, I believe, but a sense of rankling injustice would have made him move. I had been trying for three years to get him to go to my own publishing friends, and I have heard his conduct in the matter described as obstinacy. But to speak truly it was sheer weakness and nervousness. The older firm at any rate gave him fifty pounds for a book, and they were wealthy people, likely to last. My own friends were new men, and although they gave him a hundred pounds on account of increasing royalties, it was conceivably possible that they might be a failure

[1] Lawrence & Bullen, though they did not in fact publish anything of Gissing's until 1892.

and presently go out of business. His notion was that
the firm he had left would then refuse to have anything
more to do with him, that he would get no one else to
publish his work, and that he would be thrown back
into the ditch from which he had crawled with so much
difficulty. It is an odd comment on himself when he
makes one man say to another in " Paternoster Row " :
" You are the kind of man who is roused by necessity.
I am overcome by it. My nature is feeble and luxurious.
I never in my life encountered and overcame a practical
difficulty." He spoke afterwards somewhat too bitterly
of his earlier publishing experiences, and was never tired
of quoting Mrs. Gaskell to show how Charlotte Brontë
had fared.

In " The Meditations " he says : " Think of that
grey, pinched life, the latter years of which would have
been so brightened had Charlotte Brontë received but,
let us say, one-third of what, in the same space of time,
the publisher gained by her books. I know all about
this ; alas ! no man better." There was no subject on
which he was more bitterly vocal. Mr. Jones-Brown,[1]
the senior partner of Messrs. Miller and Company, I
knew myself, for after I wrote " The Western Trail " it
was read by Glass and sold to them for fifty pounds.
When this bargain was finally struck Mr. Jones-Brown
said to me : " Now, Mr. H.,[2] as the business is all
done, would you mind telling me quite frankly to what
extent this book of yours is true ? " I replied : " It is
as true in every detail as it can possibly be." " Then
you mean to say," he asked, " that you actually did
starve as you relate ? " I said : " Certainly I did, and
I might have made it a deal blacker if I had chosen."
He fell into a momentary silent reverie and shaking his

---

[1] Presumably George Smith (1824–1901).
[2] Mr. R. (*i.e.* Roberts).

head, murmured : " Ah, hunger is a dreadful thing ;— I once went without dinner myself ! " This was a favourite story of Henry Maitland's. It was so characteristic of the class he chiefly loathed. Those who have gathered by now what his satiric and ironic tendencies were, can imagine his bitter, and at the same time uproariously jocular comments on such a statement. For he was the man who had stood cursing outside a cookshop without even a penny to satisfy his raging hunger, as he truly relates under cover of " The Meditations."

It is an odd, and perhaps even remarkable fact, that the man who had suffered in this way, and was so wonderfully conscious of the absurdities and monstrosities of our present social system, working by the pressure of mere economics, should have regarded all kinds of reform not merely without hope, but with actual terror. As he owned, he had once been touched by Socialism, probably of a purely academic kind ; and yet, when he was afterwards withdrawn from such stimuli as had influenced him to think in terms of sociology, he went back to his more natural despairing conservative frame of mind. He lived in the past, and was conscious every day that something in the past that he loved was dying and must vanish. No form of future civilisation, whatever it might be, which was gained by means implying the destruction of what he chiefly loved, could ever appeal to him. He was not even able to believe that the gross and partial education of the populace was better than no education at all, in that it might some day lead to better education and a finer type of society. It was for that reason that he was a Conservative. But he was the kind of Conservative who would now be repudiated by those who call themselves such, except perhaps in some belated and befogged country house.

A non-combative Tory seems a contradiction in words, but Maitland's loathing of disturbance in any form, or of any solution of any question by means other than the criticism of the Pure Reason, was most extreme. As for his feelings towards the Empire and all that it implies, they are best put in a few words he wrote to me about my novel " In the Sun " [1] : " Yes, this is good, but you know that I loathe the Empire, and that India and Africa are an abomination to me." To anticipate as I tell his story I may quote again on the same point from a letter written to me in later years when he was in Paris : " I am very seriously thinking of trying to send my boy to some part of the world where there is at least a chance of his growing up an honest farmer without obvious risk of his having to face the slavery of military service. I would greatly rather never see him again than foresee his marching in ranks ; butchering, or to be butchered." [2]

This implies, of course, that he failed for ever to grasp the world as it was. He clung passionately and with revolt to his own ideas of what it ought to be, and protested with a curious feeble violence against the actual world as he would not see it. It is a wonder that he did anything at all. If he had had fifty pounds a year of his own he would have retreated into a remote cottage and asphyxiated himself with books.

The most painful thing in all his work was what he insisted on so often in " Paternoster Row " with regard to the poor novelist there depicted. The man was always destroying commenced work. Once he speaks about " writing a page or two of manuscript daily, with several holocausts to retard him." Within my certain knowledge this happened scores of times to Maitland.

[1] I do not know which of Roberts's novels is here intended, unless it be *A Son of Empire* (1900).
[2] See note, p. 95. (*R.*)

He burnt a quarter of a volume, half a volume, three-quarters of a volume, a whole volume, and even more, time and time again. He did this because he fancied nervously that he must write, that he had to write, and therefore began without adequate preparation. It became absolutely tragic, for he began work knowing that he would destroy it, and knowing the pain such destruction would cost him, when a little rest might have enabled him to begin cheerfully with a fresh mind. I used to suggest this to him, but it was entirely useless to advise him. He would begin, and destroy, and begin again, and then only partially satisfy himself at last when he was in a state of financial desperation, with the ditch or the workhouse in front of him. Moreover, he suffered, as most writers suffer, from a periodical feeling that he could do no more, that he had come at last to the end of his tether.

In this he never seemed to learn by experience. It grew out of a native futility, which was all the odder because he was so peculiarly conscious of a certain kind of futility exhibited by our friend Schmidt. He used to write to Maitland from Potsdam at least a dozen times a year. These letters were almost invariably read to me. They afforded Maitland amusement and real pleasure and yet great pain. Schmidt used to begin the letter with something like this : " I have been spending the last month or two in deep meditation on the work which it lies in my power to do. I have now discovered that I was not meant to write fiction. I am therefore putting it resolutely aside, and am turning to history, to which I shall henceforward devote my life." About two months later Maitland would read me a portion of a letter which began : " I have been much troubled these last two months, and have been considering my own position and my own endowments with the greatest interest. I find that I have been mistaken in thinking that I had any powers which would enable me to write history in a satisfactory manner. I see that I am essentially a philosopher. Henceforth I shall devote myself to philosophy." Again, a month or two after, there would come a letter from him saying : " I am glad to tell you that I have at last discovered my own line. After much thought I am putting aside philosophy. Henceforward I devote myself to fiction." This kind of thing occurred not once but twenty or thirty times, and the German for ever wrote as if he had never written anything before with regard to his own powers and capabilities. One is reminded forcibly of a similar case in England, that of J. K. Stephen.

As I have been speaking of " Paternoster Row," it may be observed that Maitland was frequently writing directly of himself in that book. It is noteworthy that in this, one of his most successful novels, he should have recognised his own real limitations. He says that " no native impulse had directed him to novel-writing. His intellectual temper was that of the student, the scholar, but strongly blended with a love of independence which had always made him think with detestation of a teacher's life." He goes on to speak of the stories which his hero wrote, " scraps of immature psychology, the last thing a magazine would accept from an unknown man." It may be that he was thinking here of some of his own short stories, for which I was truly responsible. Year after year I suggested that he should do some, as they were, on the whole, the easiest way of making a little money. I had amazing trouble with him because it was a new line, but I returned to the charge in season and out of season, every Sunday and every week-day that I saw him, and every time I wrote him a letter. We were both perfectly conscious that he had not the art of writing dramatic short stories which might be popular. When one goes through his shorter work one discovers few indeed which are stories or properly related to the *conte*. They are, indeed, often scraps of psychology, sometimes perhaps a little crude, but the crudeness is mostly in the construction. They resemble rather possible passages from a book than short stories. Nevertheless he did fairly well with these when he worked with an agent, which he arranged finally and at last on continued pressure from me. I notice, however, that in his published volumes of short stories there are several missing which might be preserved. I do not know whether they are good, but two or three that I remember vaguely were published, I believe, in the old " Temple Bar." One was a story about a donkey, which I entirely forget, and another was called " Mr. Quy." [1] It concerned a poor man, not wholly sane, who lived in one room and left all that room contained to some one else upon his death. On casual search nothing valuable was found, but the heir or heiress discovered at last on the top of an old cupboard Quy's curious name written large in piled halfcrowns.

It may have been noticed by some that in the little " Gillman " set of verses which I have quoted he spoke of " Hendersonian bores." This perhaps requires comment. For one who loved his Rabelais and the free-spoken classics of our own tongue, Maitland had an extreme purity of thought and speech. No one, I think, would have dared to tell him a gross story, which did not possess remarkable wit or literary merit, more than once. His reception of such tales was never cordial, and I remember his peculiar and astounding indigna-

---

[1] The " story about a donkey " was *Letty Coe*, first printed in *Temple Bar*, August 1891.

tion at one incident. Somehow or other he had become acquainted with an East End clergyman named Henderson. This Henderson had, I believe, read " The Under-World," or one of the books dealing with the kind of parishioner with whom he was acquainted, and had written to Maitland. In a way they became friends, or at any rate acquaintances, for the clergyman too was peculiarly lonely. He occasionally came to 7 K, and I myself met him there. He was a man wholly misplaced, in fact he was an absolute atheist. Still, he had a cure of souls somewhere the other side of the Tower, and laboured, as I understood, not unfaithfully. He frequently discussed his mental point of view with Maitland and often used to write to him. By some native kink in his mind he used to put indecent words into these letters. I suppose he thought it was a mere outspoken literary habit. As a matter of fact this enraged Maitland so furiously that he brought the letters to me, and showing them demanded my opinion as to how he should treat them and the writer. He said : " This kind of conduct is outrageous ! What am I to do about it ? " Now, it never occurred to Maitland in a matter like this, or indeed in any matter, to be absolutely outspoken and straightforward. He was always so afraid of hurting people's feelings. I said : " It is perfectly obvious what to do. My good man, if you don't like it, write and tell him that you don't." This was to him a perfectly impossible solution of a very great difficulty. How it was solved I do not exactly remember, but I do know that we afterwards saw very little of Mr. Henderson, who is embalmed, like a poor fly, in the " Gillman " poem.

It was characteristic, and one of the causes of his continued disastrous troubles that Maitland was incapable of being abruptly or strenuously straightforward.

A direct " No," or " This shall not be done," seemed to him, no doubt, to invite argument and struggle, the one thing he invariably procured for himself by invariably trying to avoid it.

" Paternoster Row " was written, if I remember rightly, partly in 1890, and finished in 1891, in which year it was published. He was married to his second wife in March 1891,[1] shortly before this book came out. In the third volume [2] there is practically a strange and bitter, and very remarkable, forecast of the result of that marriage, showing that whilst Maitland's instincts and impulses ran away with him, his intellect was yet clear and cold. It is the passage where the hero suggests that he should have married some simple, kind-hearted work-girl. He says, " We should have lived in a couple of poor rooms somewhere, and—we should have loved each other." Whereupon Gifford— here Maitland's intellect—exclaims upon him for a shameless idealist, and sketches, most truly the likely issue of such a marriage, given Maitland or Reardon.[3] He says : " To begin with, the girl would have married you in firm persuasion that you were a ' gentleman ' in temporary difficulties, and that before long you would have plenty of money to dispose of. Disappointed in this hope, she would have grown sharp-tempered, querulous, selfish. All your endeavours to make her understand you would only have resulted in widening the impassable gulf. She would have misconstrued your every sentence, found food for suspicion in every harmless joke, tormented you with the vulgarest forms of jealousy. The effect upon your nature would have been degrading." Never was anything more true.

[1] See note 1, p. 125.
[2] *New Grub Street*, chapter XXVII.
[3] Reardon, in *New Grub Street*.

# VIII

WHATEVER kind of disaster his marriage was to be for Maitland, there is no doubt that it was for me also something in the nature of a catastrophe. There are marriages and marriages. By some of them a man's friend gains, and by others he loses, and these are the more frequent, for it is one of the curiosities of human life that a man rarely finds his friend's wife sympathetic. As it was, I knew that in a sense I had now lost Henry Maitland, or had partially lost him, to say the least of it. Unfair as it was to the woman, I felt very bitter against her, and he knew well that it was so. Thinking of her as he did, anything like free human intercourse with his new household would be impossible, unless, indeed, the affair turned out otherwise than I expected. And then he had left London and gone to his beloved Devonshire. How much he loved it those who have read " The Meditations " can tell, for all that is said there about that county was very sincere, as I can vouch for. Born in a grim part of Yorkshire, and brought up in Mirefields and Moorhampton, that rainy and gloomy city of the north, he loved the sweet southern county. And yet it is pleasing to recognise what a strange passion was his for London. He had something of the same passion for it as Johnson, although the centre of London for him was not Fleet Street but the British Museum and its great library. He wrote once to his doctor friend : " I dare not settle far from London, as it means ill-health to me to be out of reach of the literary ' world '—a small world enough, truly." But it was most extraordinarily his world. He was a natural bookworm compelled to spin fiction. And yet he did love the country, though he now found no peace there. With his wife peace was impossible, and this I soon learnt from little things that he wrote to me, though for the first few months of his marriage he was exceedingly delicate on this subject, as if he were willing to give her every chance. I was down in Devonshire only once while he was there with his wife. I went in a steamship to Dartmouth, entering its narrow and somewhat hazardous harbour in the middle of the great blizzard which in that year overwhelmed the south of England, and especially the south of Devon, in the heaviest snow drifts. When I did at last get away from Dartmouth, I found things obviously not all they should be, though very little was said about his wife. I remember we went for a walk together, going through paths cut in snow drifts twelve or even fifteen feet in depth. Though such things had been a common part of some of my own experiences they were wonderfully new and exhilarating to Maitland. I did not stay long in Devon, nor, as a matter of fact, did he. For though he had gone there meaning to settle, he found the lack of the British Museum and his literary world too much for him, and besides that his wife, a girl of the London streets and squares, loathed the country, and whined in her characteristic manner about its infinite dullness. Thus it was that he soon left the west and took a small house in Ewell,[1] about which he wrote me constant jeremiads.

He believed, with no rare ignorance, as those who are acquainted with the methods of the old cathedral builders will know, that all honest work had been done long ago, that all ancient builders were honourable

---

[1] Or Epsom (*Eversley*, Worple Road) : September 1894, until early in 1897.

men, and that modern work was essentially unsound.
He had never learned that the first question the instructed ask the attendant verger on entering a cathedral
is : " When did the tower fall down ? " It rarely
happens that one is not instantly given a date, not
always very long after that particular tower was completed. I remember that it annoyed him very much
when I proved to him by documentary evidence that a
great portion of the work in Peterborough Cathedral
was of the most shocking and scandalous description.
But these facts do not excuse the modern jerry-builders,
and the condition of his house was one, though only
one, of the perpetual annoyances he had to encounter.

Yet, after all, though pipes burst and the roof leaks,
that is nothing if peace dwells in a house. There could
be no peace in Maitland's house, for his wife had neither
peace nor any understanding. She was an uneducated
woman. She had read nothing but what such people
read. It is true she did not speak badly. For some
reason she was not wholly without aspirates. Nevertheless many of her locutions were vulgar, and she had
no natural refinement. This, I am sure, would have
mattered little, and perhaps nothing, if she had been a
simple housewife, some actual creature of the kitchen
like Rousseau's Thérèse. It is my opinion that Maitland
was really incapable of a great passion, and I am sure
that he would have put up with the merest haus-frau,
if she had known her work and possessed her patient
soul in quiet without any lamentations. If there was
any lamenting to be done Maitland himself might
have done it in choice terms not without humour.
And indeed he did lament, and not without cause.
On my first visit to Ewell after his return from Devon
I again met Mrs. Maitland. She made me exceedingly
uneasy, both personally, as I had no sympathy with

her, and also out of fear for his future. It did not take me long to discover that they were then living on the verge of a daily quarrel, that a dispute was for ever imminent, and that she frequently broke out into actual violence and the smashing of crockery. While I was with them she perpetually made whining and complaining remarks to me about him in his very presence. She said : " Henry does not like the way I do this, or the way I say that." She asked thus for my sympathy, casting bitter looks at her husband. On one occasion she even abused him to my face, and afterwards I heard her anger in the passage outside, so that I at last hated her and found it very hard to be civil.

By this time I had established a habit of never spending any time in the company of folks who neither pleased nor interested me. I commend this custom to any one who has any work to do in the world. Thus my forthcoming refusal to see any more of her was anticipated by Maitland, who had a powerful intuition of the feelings I entertained for his wife. In fact, things became so bad that he found it necessary to speak to me on the subject, as it was nearly impossible for him to let any one enter his house for fear of an exhibition of rage, or even of possible incivility to the guest himself. As he said, she developed the temper of a devil, and began to make his life not less wretched, though in another way, than the poor creature now in her grave had made it. Naturally, however, as we had been together so much, I could not and would not give up seeing him. But we had to meet at the station, and going to the hotel would sit in the smoking-room to have our talk. These talks were now not wholly of books or of work, but often of his miseries. One day when I found him especially depressed he complained that it was almost impossible for him to get sufficient

peace to do any writing. On hearing this the notion
came to me that, though I had been unable to prevent
him from marrying this woman, I might at any rate
suggest that he should take his courage in both hands
and leave her. But I was in no hurry to put this into
his head so long as there seemed any possibility of
some kind of peace being established. However, she
grew worse daily, so at last I spoke.

He answered my proposal in accents of despair, and
I found that he was now expecting within a few months
his first [1] child's birth. Under many conditions this
might have been a joy to him, but now it was no joy.
And yet there was, he said, some possibility that after
this event things might improve. I recognised such a
possibility without much hope of its ever becoming a
reality. It was a vain hope. It is true that for a time,
the month or so while she was still weak after childbirth,
she was unable to be actively offensive ; but, honestly,
I think the only time he had any respite was before
she was able to get up and move about the house.
During the last weeks of her convalescence she vented
her temper and exercised her uncivil tongue upon the
nurses, more than one of whom left the house, finding
it impossible to stay with her. However, he was at
any rate more or less at peace in his own writing-room
during this period. When she again became well I
gathered the real state of the case from him both from
letters and conversations, and saw that eventually he
would and must leave her. Knowing him as I did,
I was aware that there would be infinite trouble, pain,
and worry before this was accomplished, and yet the
symptoms of the whole situation pointed out the
inevitable end. I had not the slightest remorse in doing

[1] Second—an obvious lapse of memory, for on p. 153 Roberts speaks of " the
boy " as being nearly three years old in 1895. Actually he has somewhat confused two boys—one born late in 1891, the other late in 1895.

my best to bring this about, but in those days I had trouble enough of my own, and found it impossible to see him as often as I wished ; especially as a visit from me, or from anybody else, always meant the loss of a day's work to him. Yet I know that he bore ten thousand times more than I would have borne in similar circumstances, and I shall give a wrong impression of him if any one thinks that most of his complaints and confessions were not dragged out of him by me. He did not always complain readily, but one saw the trouble in his eyes. At last it became evident that he would and must revolt. It grew so clear that I wanted him to do it at once and save himself years of misery, but to act like that, not wholly out of pressing and urgent necessity but out of wisdom and foresight, was wholly beyond Henry Maitland.

It was in such conditions that the child was born and spent the first months of its life. Those who have read his books, and have seen the painful paternal interest he has more than once depicted, will understand how bitterly he felt that his child, the human being for whose existence he was responsible, should be brought up in such conditions by a mother whose temper and conduct suggested almost actual madness. He wrote to me : " My dire need at present is for a holiday. It is five years since I had a real rest from writing, and I begin to feel worn out. It is not only the fatigue of inventing and writing ; at the same time I keep house and bring up the boy,[1] and the strain, I can assure you, is rather severe. What I am now trying to do is to accumulate money enough to allow of my resting, at all events from this ceaseless production, for half a year or so. It profits me nothing to feel that there is a market for my work, if the work itself tells so

---

[1] *I.e.* the first boy.

severely upon me. Before long I shall really be unable
to write at all. I am trying to get a few short stories
done, but the effort is fearful. The worst of it is, I
cannot get away by myself. It makes me very uncomfortable to leave the house, even for a day. I foresee
that until the boy is several years older there will be
no possibility of freedom for me. Of one thing I have
very seriously thought, and that is whether it would
be possible to give up housekeeping altogether, and
settle as boarders in some family on the Continent.
The servant question is awful, and this might be an
escape from it, but of course there are objections. I
might find all my difficulties doubled."

I do not think that this letter requires much comment
or illustration. Although it is written soberly enough,
and without actual accusation, its meaning is as plain
as daylight. His wife was alternately too familiar,
or at open hostility, with the servant; none could
endure her temper. She complained to him, or the
servant complained to him, and he had to make peace,
or to try to make it—mostly in vain. And then the
quarrel broke out anew, and the servant left. The
result was that Maitland often did the household work
when he should have been writing. He was dragged
away from his ordinary tasks by an uproar in the
kitchen; or perhaps one or both of the angry women
came to him for arbitration about some point of common decency. There is a phrase of his in " The Meditations " which speaks of poor Hooker, whose prose he
so much admired, being " vixen-haunted." This
epithet of his is a reasonable and admirable one, but
how bitter it was few know so well as myself.

In this place it does not seem to me unnatural or
out of place to comment a little on Raymond,[1] the

[1] Rolfe.

chief character in " The Vortex." He was undoubtedly in a measure the later Maitland. His idea was to present a man whose character developed with somewhat undue slowness. He said that Raymond would probably never have been developed at all after a certain stage but for the curious changes wrought in his views and sentiments by the fact of his becoming a father. It must be obvious to anyone, from what I have said, that Maitland himself would hardly have remained so long with his second wife after the first few months if it had not been that she was about to become a mother. The earlier passages in " The Vortex " where he speaks about children, or where Raymond speaks about them, are meant to contrast strongly with his way of thinking in the later part of the book when this particular character had children of his own. The author declared that Raymond, as a bachelor, was largely an egoist. The truth of the matter is that Maitland himself was essentially an egoist. I once suggested to him that he came near being a solipsist, a word he probably had never heard of till then, as he never studied psychology, modern or otherwise. However, when Raymond grew riper in the experience which killed his crude egoism, he became another man. Maitland, in writing about this particular book, said : " That Raymond does nothing is natural to the man. The influences of the whirlpool—that is London—and its draft on the man's vitality embarrass any efficiency there might have been in him." Through the whole story of Maitland one feels that everything that was in any way hostile to his own views of life did essentially embarrass, and almost make impossible, anything that was in him. He had no strength to draw nutriment by main force from everything around him, as a strong man does. He was not so fierce a fire as to burn all kinds of fuel.

I remember in this connection a very interesting passage in Hamley's " Operations of War " : " When a general surveying the map of the theatre finds direct obstacles in the path he must advance by, he sees in them, if he be confident of his skill in manœuvring, increased opportunities for obtaining strategical successes . . . in fact, like any other complications in a game, they offer on both sides additional opportunities to skill and talent, and additional embarrassments to incapacity." But then Maitland loathed and hated and feared obstacles of every kind. He was apt to sit down before them wringing his hands, and only desperation moved him, not to attack, but to elude them. He played no games, and despised them with peculiar vigour. Thus he never learnt that a passive defence must inevitably lose. There is a passage in one of his letters to Rivers about a certain Evans, mentioned with a note of exclamation, and thus kindly embalmed: "Evans, strange being ! Yet, if his soul is satisfied with golf and bridge, why should he not go on golfing and bridging ? At all events he is working his way to sincerity."

The long letter I quoted from above was written, I believe, in 1895, when the boy was nearly three years old.[1] I have not attempted, and shall not attempt, to give any detailed account month by month, or even year by year, of his domestic surroundings. It was a wonder to me that the marriage lasted, but still it did last, and all one knew was that some day it must come to an end. The record of his life in these days would be appalling if I remembered it sufficiently, or had kept a diary—as no doubt I ought to have done—or had all the documents which may be in existence dealing with that time. That he endured so many

[1] See note to p. 149.

years was incredible, but still he did endure, and the time went on, and he worked ; mostly, as he said to me, against time, and a good deal on commission. He wrote : " The old fervours do not return to me, and I have got into the very foolish habit of perpetually writing against time and to order. The end of this is destruction." But still I think he knew within him that it could not last. Had it not been for the boy, and, alas, for the birth of yet another son, he would now have left her. He acknowledged it to me—if he could not fight he would have to flee.

This extraordinary lack of power to deal with any obstacle must seem strange to most men, though no doubt many are weak. Yet few are so weak as Maitland. I have heard the idea expressed that there was more power of fight in Maitland than he ever possessed, and on inquiry I have learned that this notion was founded on a partial, or perhaps complete misunderstanding of certain things he expressed in the latter part of " The Vortex." Towards the end of the book it seems to be suggested that Maitland, or Raymond, tended really towards what he calls in one of his letters a " barrack-room " view of life. Some people seem to think that the man who was capable of writing what he did in that book really meant it, and must have had a little touch of that native and natural brutality which makes Englishmen what they are. But Maitland himself, in commenting on this particular attitude of Raymond, declared that this quasi or semi-ironic imperialism of the man was nothing but his hopeless recognition of facts which filled him with disgust. The world was going in a certain way. There was no refusing to see it. It stared every one in the eyes. Then he adds : " But *what* a course for things to take ! "

Raymond in fact talks with a little throwing up of

the arm, and in a voice of quiet sarcasm, " Go ahead—
I sit by and watch, and wonder what will be the end
of it all." This was his own habit of mind in later
years. He had come at last and at long last, to recognise a state of things which formerly he could not, or
would not, perceive ; and he recognised it with just
that tossing of arm or head, involuntary of course. I
do not think that at this time he would have seen a
battalion of Guards go by and have turned to me
saying : " And *this*, this is the nineteenth century ! "
He once wrote to Rivers, what he had said a hundred
times to me : " I have a conviction that all I love and
believe in is going to the devil. At the same time I
try to watch with interest this process of destruction,
admiring any bit of sapper work that is well done." It
is amusing to note that in the letter, written in the
country, which puts these things most dolefully, he
adds : " The life here shows little trace of vortical
influence." Of course this is a reference to the whirlpool
of London.

In 1896 I was myself married, and went to live in
Fulham. I understood what peace was, and he had
none. As Maitland had not met my wife for some
years I asked him to come and dine with us. It was
not the least heavy portion of his burden that he always
left his own house with anxiety and went back to it
with fear and trembling. This woman of his home was
given to violence, even with her own young children. It
was possible, as he knew, for he often said so to me, that
he might return and find even the baby badly injured.
And yet at last he made up his mind to accept my
invitation. Whether it was due to the fact that he had
accepted one from me—and I often fancy his wife had
a grudge against me because I would not go to her
house any more—I do not know, but when he came I

found him in the most extraordinary state of nervous and physical agitation. Though usually of a remarkable, if healthy, pallor, he was now almost crimson, and his eyes sparkled with furious indignation. He was hot, just as if he had come out of an actual physical struggle. What he must have looked like when he left Ewell I do not know, for he had had all the time necessary to travel from there to Fulham to cool down in. After shaking hands he asked me, almost breathlessly, to allow him to wash his face, so I took him into the bathroom. He removed his coat, and producing his elastic band from his waistcoat pocket, put it about his hair like a fillet, and began to wash in cold water. As he was drying himself he broke out suddenly : " I can't stand it any more. I have left her for ever." I said : " Thank heaven that you have. I am very glad of it—and for every one's sake don't go back on it."

Whatever the immediate cause of this outburst was, it seems that in that afternoon the whole trouble came to a culmination. The wife behaved like a maniac ; she shrieked, and struck him. She abused him in the vilest terms, such as he could not or would not repeat to me. It was with the greatest difficulty that I got him calm enough to meet any one else. When he did calm down after he had something to eat and a little to drink, the prospect of freedom, which he believed had come to him once more, inspired him with pathetic and peculiar exhilaration. In one sense he was happy that night. He slept in London.

I should have given a wholly false impression of Maitland if any one were now to imagine that I believed that the actual end had come to his marriage. No man knew his weakness better, and I moved heaven and earth in my endeavours to keep him to his resolution, to prevent him from going back to Epsom on any pretext, but all my efforts were vain. In three days I learned that his resolution had broken down. By the help of some busybody who had more kindness than intelligence, they patched up a miserable peace, and he went back to Ewell. And yet that peace was no peace. Maitland, perhaps the most sensitive man alive, had to endure people in the neighbouring houses coming out upon the doorstep, eager to inquire what disaster was occurring in the next house. There were indeed legends in the Epsom Road that the mild looking writer beat and brutalised his wife, though most knew, by means of servants' chatter, what the actual facts were.

It was in this year that he did at last take an important step which cost him much anxiety before putting it through. His fears for his eldest child were so extreme that he induced his people in the north to give the child a home which would be free from the influence and example of the mother. His wife parted with the child without any great difficulty, though, of course, she made it an occasion for abusing her husband in every conceivable way. He wrote to me in the late summer of that year : " I much want to see you, but just now it is impossible for me to get to town, and the present discomfort of everything here forbids me to ask you to come. I am straining every nerve to get some work done, for really it begins to be a question whether I shall ever again finish a book. Interruptions are so frequent and so serious. The so-called holiday has been no use to me ; a mere waste of time—but I was obliged to go, for only in that way could I have a few weeks with the boy, who, as I have told you, lives now at Mirefields and will continue to live there. I shall never let him come back to my own dwelling. Have patience with me, old friend, for I am hard beset." He ends

this letter with : " If the boy grows up in clean circumstances, that will be my one satisfaction."

Whether he had peace or not he still worked pro-
digiously, though not perhaps for so many hours as was
his earlier custom.  But his health about this time began
to fail.  Much of this came from his habits of work,
which were entirely incompatible with continued health
of brain and body.  He once said to Rivers : " Visitors
—I fall sick with terror in thinking of them.  If by rare
chance any one comes here it means to me the loss of
a whole day, a most serious matter."  And his whole
day was a very long day.  No man of letters can possibly
sit for ever at the desk during eight hours, as was frequently " his brave custom " as he phrased it somewhere.
If he had worked in a more reasonable manner, and
had been satisfied with doing perhaps a thousand words
a day, which is not an unreasonably small amount for
a man who works steadily through most of the year,
his health might never have broken down.  He had
been moved in a way towards these hours, partly by
actual desperation ; partly by the great loneliness which
had been thrust upon him ; very largely by the want
of money which prevented him from amusing himself
in the manner of the average man, but chiefly by his
sense of devotion to what he was doing.  One of his
favourite stories was that of Heyne, the great classical
scholar, who was reported to work sixteen hours a day.
This he did, according to the literary tradition, for the
whole of his working life, except upon the day when he
was married.  He made, for that occasion only, a com-
pact with the bride that he was to work half his usual
stint.  And half Heyne's usual amount was Maitland's
whole day, which I maintain was at least five hours too
much.  This manner of working, combined with his
quintessential and habitual loneliness, made it very

hard, not only for him, but also for his friends. It was quite impossible to see him, even about matters of comparative urgency, unless a meeting had been arranged beforehand. For even after his work was done, it was never done. He started preparing for the next day, turning over phrases in his mind, and considering the next chapter. In one point I was very useful to him, for I suggested, as I have done to others, that my own practice of finishing a chapter and then writing some two or three lines of the next one, while my mind was warm upon the subject, was a vast help for the next day's labour.

Now the way he worked was this. After breakfast, at nine o'clock, he sat down and slaved till one. Then he had his midday meal, and took a little walk. In the afternoon, about half-past three, he sat down again and wrote till six o'clock or a little after. Then he worked again from half-past seven to ten. I doubt if there is any modern writer who has ever tried to keep up work at this rate who did not end in a hospital or a lunatic asylum, or die young. To my mind it shows, in a way that nothing else can, that he had no earthly business to be writing novels and spinning things largely out of his subjective mind, when he ought to have been dealing with the objective world, or with books. Maitland used to write three or four of his slips, as he called them, which were small quarto pages of very fine paper, and on each slip there were twelve hundred words. Whether he wrote one, or two, or three slips in the day he took an equal length of time.

Among my notes I find one about a letter of his written in June 1895 to Mrs. Lake, declining an invitation to visit Dr. Lake's house, though such an interlude, no doubt, would have done him a great deal of good. He says : " Let me put before you an appalling list of things that have to be done. (1) Serial story (only begun) of about eighty thousand words. (2) Short novel for Cassell's [1] to be sent in by end of October. Neither begun nor thought of. (3) Six short stories for the *English Illustrated* [2]—neither begun nor thought of. (4) Twenty papers for *The Sketch* of a thousand words each. Dimly foreseen." Now to a man who had the natural gift of writing fiction and some reasonable time to do it in, this would seem no such enormous amount of work. For Maitland it was appalling, not so much, perhaps, on account of the actual amount of labour— if it had been one book—but for its variousness. He moved from one thing to another in fiction with great slowness.

All this time his health was not satisfactory. I shall have something to say about this in detail a little later. It was his own opinion, and that of certain doctors, that his lungs were really affected by tuberculosis. Of this I had then very serious doubts. But he wrote in January 1897 : " The weather and my lung are keeping me indoors at present, but I should much like to come to you. Waterpipes freezing—a five-pound note every winter to the plumber. Of course this is distinctly contrived by the building fraternity."

But things were not always so bad as may be gathered from a casual consideration of what I have said. In writing a life events come too thickly. For instance in 1897 he wrote to me : " Happily things are far from being as bad as last year." It appears that a Miss Greathead,[3] about whom I know nothing but what he told me, interested herself with the utmost kindness in his domestic affairs. Part of his letter ran : " Miss Greathead has been of very great use, and will continue

---

[1] *The Paying Guest* (1895).
[2] The *English Illustrated News*.
[3] Probably Miss Orme : a pseudonymous formation of Llandudnovian origin.

to be so, I think. This house is to be given up in any case at Michaelmas, and another will not be taken till I see my way more clearly. Where I myself shall live during the autumn is uncertain. We must meet in the autumn. Work on—I have plans for seven books."

# IX

WHAT dismal catastrophe or prolonged domestic uproar led to the final end of his married life in 1897 I do not know. Nor have I cared to inquire very curiously. The fact remains, and it was inevitable. Towards the end of the summer he made up his mind to go to Italy in September. He wrote to me : " All work in England is at an end for me just now. I shall be away till next spring—looking forward with immense delight to solitude. Of course I have a great deal to do as soon as I can settle, which I think will be at Siena first." As a matter of fact the very next letter of his which I possess came to me from Siena. He said : " I am so confoundedly hard at work upon the Novelists [1] book that I find it very difficult to write my letters. Thank heaven, more than half is done. I shall go south about the tenth of November. It is dull here, and I should not stay for the pleasure of it. You know that I do not care much for Tuscany. The landscape is never striking about here, and one does not get the glorious colour of the south." So one sees how Italy had awakened his colour sense. As I have said, it was after his first visit to Italy that I noted, both in his books and his conversation, an acute awakening passion for colour. It grew in him to the end of his life. He ended this last letter to me with : " Well, well, let us get as soon as possible into Magna Græcia and the old dead world."

I said some time ago that I had finished with the Victorian novelists, and yet I find there is something

[1] *Charles Dickens* (1898).

still to say of Dickens. It is not against the plan of such
a rambling book as this to put it down here and now.
When he went to Siena to write his book of criticism
it seemed a very odd choice of a place for such work,
and indeed I wondered at his undertaking it at any
price. It is obvious to all who understand his attitude
towards criticism of modern things that great as his
interest was in Dickens it would never have impelled
him to write a strong critical book mostly about him
had it not been for the necessity of making money.
Indeed he expressed so much to me, and I find again
in a letter that he wrote to Mrs. Rivers, with whom he
was now on very friendly terms, " I have made a good
beginning with my critical book, and long to have done
with it, for, of course, it is an alien subject." No doubt
there are at least two classes of Maitland's readers,
those who understand the man and love his really characteristic work, and those who have no understanding
of him at all, or any deep appreciation, but profess a
great admiration for this book, which they judge by the
part on Dickens.[1] Probably Andrew Lang was one of
these, judging from a criticism that he once wrote on
Maitland. I know that I have often heard people of
intelligence express so high an opinion of the " Victorian
Novelists " as to imply a lack of appreciation of his
other work. The study is no doubt written with much
skill, and with a good writer's command of his subject,
and command of himself. That is to say, he manages
by skill to make people believe he was sufficiently interested in his subject to write about it. To speak plainly,
he thought it a sheer waste of time, except from the
merely financial point of view, just as he did his cutting
down of Mayhew's " Life of Dickens." [2] This, indeed,

[1] Actually, of course, the whole book is about Dickens.
[2] Forster's *Life of Dickens*.

he considered a gross outrage, but professed his inability to refuse the " debauched temptation " of the hundred and fifty pounds offered him for the work.

It would be untrue to suggest that he was not enthusiastic about Dickens, even more so than I myself save at certain times and seasons. Dickens is a man for times and periods. I cannot read him for years, and then I read all his novels one after the other. What I do mean is that Maitland's love of this author, or of Thackeray, would never have impelled him to write about them. Yet there is much in the book which is of great interest, if it were only as matter of comment on Maitland's own self. The other day I came across one sentence which greatly struck me. In it Maitland asks the reader to imagine Charles Dickens occupied in the blacking warehouse for ten years. He says : " Picture him striving vainly to find utterance for the thoughts that were in him, refused the society of any but boors and rascals, making perhaps futile attempts to succeed as an actor, and in full manhood measuring the abyss which sundered him from all he had hoped for." On coming to this passage I put the book down and pondered for a while, knowing well that as Maitland wrote these words he was thinking even more of himself than of Dickens, and knowing that what was not true of his subject was most bitterly true of the writer. There is another passage somewhere in the book in which he says that Dickens could not have struggled for long years against lack of appreciation. This he rightly puts down to Dickens' essentially dramatic leanings. The man needed immediate applause. But again Maitland was thinking of himself, for he had indeed struggled for many years without any appreciation save that of one or two friends and some rare birds among the public. I sometimes think that one of Maitland's great attractions to Dickens lay in the fact, which he himself mentions and enlarges on, that Dickens treated of the lower middle class and the class immediately beneath it. This is where the great novelist was at his best, and in the same way these were the only classes that Maitland really knew well. There is in several things a singular likeness between Dickens and Maitland, though it lies not on the surface. He says that Dickens never had any command of a situation although he was so very strong in incident. This was also a great weakness of Henry Maitland. It rarely happens that he works out a powerful and dramatic situation to its final limit, though sometimes he does succeed in doing so. This failure in dealing with great situations is peculiarly characteristic of most English novelists. I have frequently noticed in otherwise admirable books by men of very considerable abilities and attainments, with tolerable command of their own language, that they have on every occasion shirked the great dramatic scene just when it was expected and needed. Perhaps this is due to the peculiar *mauvaise honte* of the English mind. To write, and yet not to give oneself away, seems to be the aim of too many writers, though the great aim of all great writing is to do, or to try to do, what they avoid. The final analysis of dreadful passion and pain comes, perhaps, too close to them. They feel the glow but also a sensation of shame in the great emotions. There are times when Maitland felt this, though perhaps unconsciously. It is at any rate certain that, like so many people, he never actually depicted with blood and tears the frightful situations of which his life was so extraordinarily full.

In an interesting passage of this book Maitland declares that great popularity was never yet attained by any one deliberately writing down to a low ideal. Above all men he knew that the artist is necessarily sincere, however poor an artist he may be. So Rousseau in his " Confessions " asserts that nothing really great can come from an entirely venal pen. I remember Maitland greatly enjoyed a story I told him about myself. While I was still a poverty-stricken and struggling writer my father, who had no knowledge whatever of the artistic temperament, although he had a very great appreciation of the best literature of the past, came to me and said seriously : " My boy, if you want money and I know you do, why do you not write ' Bow Bells Novelettes ' ? They will give you fifteen pounds for each of them." I replied, not I think without a tinge of bitterness at being so misunderstood : " My dear sir, it is as much a matter of natural endowment to be a damned fool as to be a great genius, and I am neither."

I have said that Maitland was most essentially a conservative, indeed in many ways a reactionary, if one so passive can be called that. The only actual revolutionary utterance of his mind which stands on record is in the " Victorian Novelists." It is when he is speaking of Mr. Casby [1] of the shorn locks. He wrote : " This question of landlordism should have been treated by Dickens on a larger scale. It remains one of the curses of English life, and is likely to do so till the victims of house-owners see their way to cutting, not the hair, but the throats, of a few selected specimens."

It may seem a hard thing to say, but it is a fact, that any revolutionary sentiment there was in Maitland was excited, not by any native liberalism of his mind, nor even by his sympathy for the suffering of others, but came directly out of his own personal miseries and trials. He had had to do with landlords who refused to repair their houses, and with houses which he looked upon as

[1] In *Little Dorrit*.

the result of direct and wicked conspiracy between builders and plumbers. But his words are capable of a wider interpretation than he might have given them.

If I had indeed been satisfied that this departure of Maitland's to Italy meant the end of all the personal troubles of his marriage, I should have been highly satisfied, and not displeased with any part I might have taken in bringing about so desirable a result. But, knowing him as I did, I had very serious doubts. I was well aware of what a little pleading might do with him. It was in fact possible that one plaintive letter from his wife might have brought him back again. Fortunately it was never written. The woman was even then practically mad, and though immensely difficult to manage by those friends, such as Miss Greathead and Miss Kingdon, who interested themselves in his affairs and did much more for him at critical times than I had been able to do, she never, I think, appealed to her husband. But it was extraordinary, before he went to Italy, to observe the waverings of his mind. When he was keeping his eldest boy at Mirefields, supplying his wife with money for the house, and living in lodgings at Salcombe,[1] he wrote giving a rough account of what he might do, or might have to do, and ended by saying : " Already, lodgings are telling on my nerves. I almost think I suffer less even from yells and insults in a house of my own." He even began to forget " the fifth-rate dabblers in the British gravy," for which fine phrase T. E. Brown is responsible.[2] Maitland ought to have known it and did not. It was this perpetual wavering and weakness in him which perplexed his friends, and would indeed have alienated at last very many of them had it not been for the enduring charm in all his weakness.

[1] Perhaps Salcombe, but more probably Budleigh Salterton.
[2] *Ne sit Ancillæ*, l. 5.

But he was now out of England, and those who knew him were glad to think it was so. He was, perhaps, to have a better time. Nevertheless he wrote to his friend Lake : " Yes, it is true that I am going to glorious scenes, but do not forget that I go with much anxiety in my mind—anxiety about the little children, the chances of life and death, etc., etc. It is not like my Italian travel eight years ago, when—save for cash—I was independent. I have to make a good two hundred a year apart from my own living and casual expenses. If I live I think I shall do it—but there's no occasion for merriment." Yet if it was no occasion for mere merriment it was an occasion for joy. He knew it well, and so did those know who understand the description that Maitland gave in " Paternoster Row " of the sunset at Athens.[1] It is very wonderfully painted, and as he describes it he makes Gifford say : " Stop, or I shall clutch you by the throat. I warned you before that I cannot stand these reminiscences." And this reminds me that when I wrote to him once from Naples, he replied : " You fill me with envious gloom." [2] But now, when he had finished his pot-boiler of Siena, he was going south to Naples, his " most interesting city of the modern world," and afterwards farther south to the Calabrian Hills, and the old dead world of Magna Græcia.

---

[1] *New Grub Street*, chapter XXVII.

[2] This passage has an unhappy interest for me. After his death some kind friend, whose name I need not mention, showed me a letter in which he said that when he told me he was going to Greece I displayed signs of envy and bitterness, or something to that effect, at his being able to do so. He added that he would never again tell anyone of any luck of his. It was, unhappily, very like him not to have this out with me at once, for surely no man was ever more mistaken. Not for worlds would I have gone to Greece, in which at that time I took no great interest, even if his luck and his native kindness and love of companionship over Chianti or a bottle of villainous resinous Greek wine had made him offer to pay all expenses. Wild horses would hardly have dragged me out of London just then. The truth is that the fault (if fault there was) lay on his side. He had undertaken to do something for me which implied that he would remain in town for another month or two, and his departure involved me in much difficulty. Though I refrained from saying anything, my look doubtless showed the distress which he misinterpreted. (*R.*)

As a result of that journey he gave us " Magna Græcia." [1] This book is of itself a sufficient proof that he was by nature a scholar, an inhabitant of the very old world, a discoverer of the time of the Renaissance, a Humanist, a pure man of letters, and not by nature a writer of novels or romances. Although Maitland's scholarship was rather wide than deep save in one or two lines of investigation, yet his feeling for all those matters with which a sympathetic scholarship can deal was intense and true. Once in Calabria and the south he made, and would make, great discoveries. In spite of his poverty, which comes out so often in the description of his conditions upon this journey, he loved everything he found there with a strange and wonderful and almost pathetic passion. I remember on his return how he talked to me of the far south, and of his studies in Cassiodorus. One incident in " Magna Græcia," which is related somewhat differently from what he himself told me at the time, pleased him most especially. It was when he met two men and mentioned the name of Cassiodorus, whereupon they burst out with amazement, " Cassiodorio, why *we* know Cassiodorio ! " That the name should yet be familiar to these live men of the south gratified his incomparable historic sense, and I can well remember how he threw his head back and shook his long hair with joy, and burst into one of his most characteristic roars of laughter. It was a simple incident, but it brought back to him the past.

Of all his books I love best " Magna Græcia." I always liked it much better than " The Meditations of Mark Sumner," and for a thousand reasons. For one thing it is a wholly true book. In " The Meditations," he falsified, in the literary sense, very much that he wrote. It needs to be read with a commentary or guide.

[1] *By the Ionian Sea* (1901).

But " Magna Græcia " is pure Maitland ; it is absolutely himself. It is, indeed, very nearly the Maitland
who might have been if ill luck had not pursued him
from his boyhood. Had he been a successful man on
the lines that fate pointed out to him ; had he succeeded
greatly—or nobly, as he would have said—at the
University ; had he become a tutor, a don, a notable
man among men of letters, still would he have travelled
in southern Italy and made his great pilgrimage to the
Fonte di Cassiodorio. Till he knew south Italy his
greatest pleasure had been in books. That he loved
books we all know. There, of a certainty, " The Meditations " is a true witness. But how much more he loved
the past and the remains of Greece and old, old Italy,
" Magna Græcia " proves to us almost with tears.

I think that Maitland was perhaps not a deep scholar,
for scholarship nowadays must needs be specialised if
it is to be deep. He had his prejudices, and hugged
them. The hypothesis of Wolf[1] concerning Homer
visibly annoyed him. He preferred to think of the
Iliad and the Odyssey as having been written by one
man. This came out of his love of personality—the
great ones of the past were as gods to him. All works
of art, or books, or great events were wholly theirs, for
they made even the world, and the world made them
not. Though I know that he would have loved in
many ways such a book as Gilbert Murray's " Rise of
the Greek Epic," yet Murray's fatally decisive analysis
of the Homeric legend would have pained him deeply.
On one occasion I remember sending to him, partly as
some reasonable ground for my own scepticism, but
more, I think, out of some mischievous desire to plague
him, a cleverly written pamphlet by a barrister which

[1] Friedrich August Wolf (1759–1824) suggested that the Homeric poems were
of composite authorship.

threw doubt upon the Shakespearean legend. He wrote to me : " I have read it with great indignation. Confound the fellow !—he disturbs me." But then he was essentially a conservative, and lived in an alien time.

# X

WHAT he suffered, endured, and enjoyed in Magna Græcia and his old dead world, those know who have read with sympathy and understanding. It was truly as if the man, born in exile, had gone home at last—so much he loved it, so well he understood the old days. And now once more he came back to England to a happier life, even though great anxieties still weighed him down. Yet with some of these anxieties there was joy, for he loved his children and thought very much of them, hoping and fearing. One of the very first letters I received from him on his return from Italy is dated May 7, 1898, and was written from Henley in Arden : "You have it in your power to do me a most important service. Will you on every opportunity industriously circulate the news that I am going to live henceforth in Warwickshire? It is not strictly true, but a very great deal depends on my real abode being protected from invasion. If you could inspire a newspaper paragraph. . . . I should think it impudent to suppose that newspapers cared about the matter but that they have so often chronicled my movements, and if by any chance the truth got abroad it would mean endless inconvenience and misery to me. You shall hear more in detail when I am less be-devilled." All this requires little comment. Every one can understand how it was with him.

Later in the year he wrote to me : "My behaviour is bestial, but I am so hard driven that it is perhaps excusable. All work impossible owing to ceaseless reports of mad behaviour in London. That woman was all but given in charge the other day for assaulting her landlady with a stick. My solicitor is endeavouring to get the child out of her hands. I fear its life is endangered, but, of course, the difficulty of coming to any sort of arrangement with such a person is very great. . . . Indeed I wish we could have met before your departure for South Africa. My only consolation is the thought that something or other decisive is bound to have happened before you come back, and then we will meet as in the old days, please heaven. As for me, my literary career is at an end, and the workhouse looms larger day by day. I should not care, of course, but for the boys. A bad job, a bad job." But better times were perhaps coming for him. The child that he refers to as still in the hands of his mother was his youngest boy. Much of his life at this time is lost to me because much happened while I was absent in South Africa, where I spent some months. I remember it pleased him to get letters from me from far-off places such as Bulawayo. He always had the notion that I was an extraordinarily capable person, an idea which had some truth if my practical capacities were compared with his strange want of them. By now he was not living in Warwickshire ; indeed, if I remember rightly, on my return from Africa I found him at Godalming.

When I left Cape Town I was very seriously ill, and remained ill for some months after my return home. Therefore it was some time till we met again. But when we did meet it was at Leatherhead,[1] where he was in lodgings, pleased to be not very far from George Meredith, who indeed, I think, loved him. As I think I have said, it was through Maitland that I first met Meredith. For some reason which I do not know, Maitland gave him a book of mine, " The Western

[1] Probably Dorking.

Trail," with which the old writer was much pleased.
Indeed it was in consequence of his liking for it that he
asked me to dine with him just before I went to Africa.
Maitland was not present at this dinner, he was then
still in Warwickshire ; but Meredith spoke very affectionately of him, and said many things not unpleasing
about his work.  But probably Meredith, like myself,
thought more of the man than he did of his books,
which is indeed from my point of view a considerable
and proper tribute to any writer.  Sometimes the work
of a man is greater than himself, and it seems a pity
when one meets him ; but if a man is greater than
what he does one may always expect more and some
day get it.  It was apropos of Maitland, in some way
which I cannot exactly recall, that Meredith, who was
in great form that night, and wonderful in monologue
—as he always was, more especially after he became so
deaf that it was hard to make him hear—told us a
characteristic story about two poor schoolboys.  It
appeared, said Meredith, that these boys, who came of
a clever but poverty-stricken house, did very badly at
their school because they were underfed.  As Meredith
explained this want of food led to a poor circulation.
What blood these poor boys had was required for the
animal processes of living, and did not enable them to
carry on the work of the brain in the way that it should
have done.  However, it happened that during play one
of these boys was induced to stand upon his head, with
the result that the blood naturally gravitated to that
unaccustomed quarter.  His ideas instantly became
brilliant—so brilliant, indeed, that a great idea struck
him.  He regained his feet, rushed home, communicated
his discovery to his brother, and henceforward they conducted their studies standing upon their heads, and
became brilliant and successful men.  Meredith and

Henry Maitland had one thing tremendously in common, their love of words. In my conversation with Meredith that day I mentioned the fact that I had read a certain interview with him. I asked him whether it conveyed his sentiments with any accuracy. He replied mournfully : " Yes, yes—no doubt the poor fellow got down more or less what I meant, but he used none of my beautiful words, none of my beautiful words ! "

It does not seem to me unnatural to say something of George Meredith, since he had in many ways an influence on Maitland. Certainly when it came to the question of beautiful words they were on the same ground, if not on the same level. I have met during my literary life, and in some parts of the world where literature is little considered, many men who were reputed great, and indeed were so, it may be, in some special line, yet Meredith was the only man I ever knew to whom I would have allowed freely the word " great " the moment I met him, without any reservation. This I said to Maitland and he smiled, feeling that it was true. I remember he wrote to Lake about Meredith, saying : " You ought to read ' Richard Feverel,' ' Evan Harrington,' ' The Egoist,' and ' Diana of the Crossways.' These, in my opinion, are decidedly his best books, but you won't take up anything of his without finding strong work." And " strong work " with Maitland was very high praise indeed.

By now, when he was once more in Surrey, we did not meet so infrequently as had been the case after his second marriage and before the separation. It is true that his living out of London made a difference. Still I went down sometimes and stayed a day with him. We talked once more in something of our old manner about books and words, the life of men of letters, and literary origins or pedigrees, always a strong point in him. It was always a pleasure to Maitland when he discovered the influence of one writer upon another. For instance, it was he who pointed out to me first that Balzac was the literary parent of Murger, as none indeed can deny who have read the chapter in " Illusions Perdues " where Lucien de Rubempré writes and sings the drinking song with tears in his eyes as he sits by the bedside of Coralie, his dead mistress. This he did, as will be remembered, to obtain by the sale of the song sufficient money to bury her. From that chapter undoubtedly sprang the whole of the " Vie de Bohème," though to it Murger added much, and not least his livelier sense of humour. Again, I well remember how Maitland took down Tennyson—ever a joy to him, because Tennyson was a master of words though he had little enough to say—and showed me the influence that the " Wisdom of Solomon," in the Apocrypha, had upon some of the last verses of " The Palace of Art." No doubt some will not see in a mere epithet or two that Solomon's words had any connection with the work of the Poet Laureate, whom I nicknamed, somewhat to Maitland's irritation, " the bourgeois Chrysostom." Yet there is no doubt that Maitland was right ; but even if he had not been he would still have taken wonderful joy in finding out the words of the two verses [1] which run : " Whether it were a whistling wind, or a melodious noise of birds among the spreading branches, or a pleasant fall of water running violently, or a terrible sound of stones cast down, or a running that could not be seen of skipping beasts, or a roaring voice of most savage wild beasts, or a rebounding echo from the hollow mountains ; these things made them to swoon for fear." But he loved all rhythm, and found it sometimes in unexpected places, even in unconsidered writers. There

[1] xvii. : 18, 19.

was one passage he used to quote from Mrs. Ewing, who, indeed, at her best was no small writer, which he declared to be wonderful, and in its way quite perfect : " He sat, patient of each succeeding sunset, until this aged world should crumble to its close." Then, again, he rejoiced when I discovered, though no doubt it had been discovered many times before, that his musical Keats owed much to Fletcher's " Faithful Shepherdess."

It would be a very difficult question to ask in some examination concerning English literature, what book in English by its very nature and style appealed most of all to Henry Maitland. I think I am not wrong in saying that it was undoubtedly Walter Savage Landor's " Imaginary Conversations." That book possesses to the full the two great qualities which most delighted him. It is redolent of the past, and those classic con-versations were his chief joy ; but above and beyond this true and great feeling of Landor's for the past classic times there was the most eminent quality of Landor's rhythm. I have many times heard Maitland read aloud from " Æsop and Rhodope," and have even more often heard him quote without the book the passage which runs : " There are no fields of amaranth on this side of the grave ; there are no voices, O Rhodope, that are not soon mute, however tuneful ; there is no name, with whatever emphasis of passionate love repeated, of which the echo is not faint at last." Maitland knew, and none knew better, that in a tri-umphant passage there is triumphant rhythm, and in a passage full of mourning or melancholy the accompany-ing and native rhythm is both melancholy and mournful. How many times, too, I have heard him quote, again from Landor, " Many flowers must perish ere a grain of corn be ripened."

All this time the wife was I know not where, nor did

I trouble much to inquire. Miss Kingdon and Miss Greathead looked after her very patiently, and did good work for their friend Maitland, as he well knew. But although he rejoiced to be alone for a time, or at any rate relieved from the violent misery of her presence, I came once more to discern, both from things he said and from things he wrote to me, that a celibate life began again to oppress him gravely. It was many months before he at last confided in me fully, and then he did it only because he was certain that I was the one friend he possessed with whom he could discuss any question without danger of moral theories or prepossessions interfering with the rightful solution. Over and beyond this qualification for his confidence there was the fact that I knew him, whereas no one else did. To advise any man it is necessary to know the man who is to be advised, for wisdom *in vacuo* or *in vitro* may be nothing but foolishness. Others would have said to him, " Look back on your experience and reflect. Have no more to do with women in any way." No doubt it would have been good advice, but it would have been impossible for him to act on it. Therefore when he at last opened his mind to me and told me of certain new prospects which were disclosing themselves to him, I was not only sympathetic but encouraging. It seems that in the year 1898 he first met a young French lady of Spanish origin with whom he had previously corresponded for some little time. Her name was Thérèse Espinel.[1] She belonged to a very good family, perhaps somewhat above the *haute bourgeoisie*, and was a woman of high education and extreme Gallic intelligence. As I came to know her afterwards I may also say that she was a very beautiful woman, and possessed, what I know to have been a very great charm to Maitland, as it

[1] Gabrielle Fleury (1869–1954).

always was to me, a very sweet and harmonious voice—
it was perhaps the most beautiful human voice for speaking that I have ever heard. Years afterwards I took her
to see George Meredith. He kissed her hand and told
her she had beautiful eyes. As she was partly Spanish
she knew Spanish well. Her German was excellent, her
English that of an educated Englishwoman. It appears
that she came across Maitland's " Paternoster Row,"
and it occurred to her that it should be translated into
French. She got into correspondence with him about
this book, and in 1898 came over to England and made
his acquaintance. It is interesting to know that on one
other occasion Maitland got into correspondence with
another French lady, who insisted emphatically that he
was the one person whom she could trust to direct her
aright in life—a notion at the time not a little comical
to me, and also to the man who was to be this soul's
director.

When these two people met and proved mutually
sympathetic it was not unnatural that he should tell
her something of his own life, especially when one knows
that so much of their earlier talks dealt with " Paternoster Row " and with its chief character, so essentially
Henry Maitland. He gave her, indeed, very much of
his story, yet not all of it, not, indeed, the chief part of
it, since the greatest event in his life was the early
disaster which had maimed and distorted his natural
career and development. Yet even so much as he told
her of his first and second marriages—for he by no
means concealed that he was married—very naturally
engaged her womanly compassion. Adding this to her
real and fervent admiration of his literary powers, his
personality and story seem to have inclined her to take
an even tenderer interest in him. She was certainly a
bright and wonderful creature, although not without a

certain native melancholy, and she possessed none of
those conventional ideas which wreck some lives and
save others from disaster. Therefore I was not much
surprised, although I had not been told everything that
had happened, when Maitland wrote to me that he
contemplated taking a very serious step. It was indeed
a very serious one, but so natural in the circumstances,
as I came to hear of them, that I made no strictures
on his scheme. It was no other than the proposal that
he and this new acquaintance of his should cast in their
lot together and make the world and her relatives believe
that they were married. When consulted I found it
difficult to give advice. What was advisable for the
man might not be advisable for his proposed partner.
He was making no sacrifice, and she was making many.
Nevertheless, I hold the opinion that these matters are
matters for the people concerned and are nobody else's
business. The thing to be considered from my own
point of view—that is, the happiness he might get out
of it—was whether Maitland would be able to support
her, and whether she was the kind of woman who
would retain her hold upon him and give him some
peace and comfort towards the end of his life. In thinking over these things I remembered that the other two
women had not been ladies. They had not been educated. They understood nothing of the world which
was Maitland's world, and, as I knew, a disaster was
bound to come in both cases. But now it appeared to
me that there was a possible hope for the man, that
such a step might end in happiness, or at any rate in
peace. That something of the kind would occur I knew,
and even if this present affair went no farther yet some
other woman would have to be dealt with some day
even if she did not come into his life for a long while.
Thérèse Espinel, at any rate, was really beautiful and

accomplished, essentially of the upper classes, at least of the upper bourgeoisie, and, what was no small thing from Maitland's point of view, a capable and feeling musician. Of such a woman Maitland had had only a few weeks' experience many years before. I thought the situation promised much, and raised no moral objection to the step he proposed to take as soon as I saw he was strongly bent in one direction. I felt sure that anything whatever which put a definite obstacle in the way of his returning to his wife was to be encouraged. It was, in fact, absolutely a duty ; and I care not what comments may be made upon my attitude or my morals.

That Maitland would have gone back to his wife eventually I have very little doubt, and nothing but disaster and new rage and misery would have come of his doing so. For these reasons I did everything in my power to help and encourage him in a matter which gave him extreme nervousness and anxiety. He said to me that the step he proposed to take early in 1899 grew more and more serious the more he thought of it. Again, I think there was no overwhelming passion at the back of his mind. Yet it was a true and sincere affection. But there were many difficulties. It appears that the girl's father had died a few months before, and as there was some money in the family this fact involved certain serious difficulties about the future signing of names when all the legal questions concerned with the little property came to be settled. Then he asked me what sort of hope was there that this pretended marriage would not become known in England. He said : " I fear it certainly would." When reflecting on the innumerable lies and subterfuges that I indulged in with the view of preventing anybody knowing of this affair in London, I can see that he was perfectly justified in his fears, for when the step was at last taken I was continually being asked about Maitland's wife. Naturally enough, it was said by one set of people that she was with him in France ; while it was averred by others, much better informed, that she was still in England. I was sometimes requested to settle this difficult matter, and I found it so difficult that at times I was compelled to tell the facts on condition that they were regarded as absolutely confidential.

He and Thérèse did, indeed, discuss the possibility of braving the world with the simple truth, but that he knew would have been a very tremendous step for her. The mother was yet living, and played a strange part in this little drama—a part not so uncommonly played as many might think. She became at last her daughter's *confidante* and learned the whole of Maitland's story, and, although she opposed their solution of the trouble to the very best of her power, when it became serious she at last gave way and consented to any step that her daughter wished to take, provided that there was no public scandal.

Many people will regard with horror the part that her mother played in this drama, imputing much moral blame. There are, however, times when current morality has not the value that is commonly given to it, and I think Madame Espinel acted with great wisdom, seeing that nothing she could have pleaded would have altered matters. Her daughter was no longer a child ; she was a grown-up woman, not without determination, and entirely without religious prejudice, a thing not so uncommon with intellectual Frenchwomen. Assuredly there are some who will say that a public scandal was better than secrecy, and in this I am at one with them. Still there was much to consider, for there would certainly have been what Henry himself called " a horrific scandal," seeing that the family had many aristocratic relatives. Maitland, in fact, stated that it would be taking an even greater responsibility than he was prepared to shoulder if this were done. He wrote to me asking for my opinion and counsel, especially at the time when there was a vague and probably unfounded suggestion that he might be able to get a divorce from his wife. It appears that more than one person wrote to him anonymously about her. He never believed what they told him, nor do I. From some points of view I may have been very unjust to his wife, though I have tried to hold the balance true, but I never saw, or heard from Maitland, anything to suggest that she was not all that she should have been in one way, just as she was everything she should not have been in another. Seeing that Maitland would have given ten years of his life and every penny he possessed to secure a divorce, it is certain that he absolutely disbelieved what he was told. In fact, if he could have got a divorce by consent or collusion he would have gladly engaged to pay her fifty pounds a year during his life, whatever happened and whatever she did. But this could not be said openly, either by myself or by him, and nothing came out of the suggestion, whoever made it first.

I proposed to him one afternoon when with him that he should make some inquiries as to what an American divorce would do for him. Whether it were valid or not, it might perhaps make things technically easier and enable him to marry in France with some show of legality. At the moment he paid no attention, or seemed to pay no attention, but it must have sunk into his mind, for a few days afterwards he wrote to me and said : " Is it a possible thing to get a divorce in some other country as things are ?—a divorce which would allow of a legal marriage, say in that same country ? I have vaguely heard such stories, especially of Heligoland. The German novelist, Sacher Masoch, is said to have done it—said so by his first wife, who now lives in Paris." Upon receiving this letter I reminded him of what I had said about American divorces, and gave him all the information that I had in my mind and could collect at the moment, especially mentioning Dakota and Nevada as two of the United States which had the most reasonable and wide-minded views of marriage and divorce. He wrote and thanked me heartily, but quoted from a letter of Thérèse which seemed to indicate, not unclearly, that she preferred him to take no steps which might lead to long legal processes. They should join their fortunes together, taking their chance as to the actual state of affairs being discovered afterwards. His great trouble, of course, was the absolute necessity of seeming, out of regard for her relatives, to be legally married. Besides these connections of her family, she knew a great number of important people in Paris and Madrid, and many of them should receive by custom the *lettres de faire part*. With some little trouble the financial difficulties with regard to the signing of documents were got over for the moment by a transfer of investments from Thérèse to her mother. On this being done their final determination was soon taken, and they determined, after this " marriage " was completed, to leave Paris and live somewhere in the mountains, perhaps in Savoy ; and he then wrote to me : " You will be the only man in London who knows this story. Absolute silence—it goes without saying. If ever by a slip of the tongue you let a remark fall that my wife was dead, *tant mieux* ; only no needless approach to the topic. A grave responsibility mine. She is a woman to go through fire for, as you saw. An incredible woman to one who has spent his life with such creatures. . . . I have lately paid a bill of one pound for damage done by my wife, damage in a London house where she lived till turned out by the help of the police. Incredible stories about her. She attacked the landlord with a stick, and he had seriously to defend himself. Then she tore up shrubs and creepers in the garden. No, I have had my time of misery. It must come to an end."

In the first part of this letter which I have just quoted he says, " She is a woman to go through fire for, as you saw." This expression does not mean that I had ever met her, but that I had seen sufficient of her letters to recognise the essential fineness of her character. I urged him once more to a rapid decision, and he promised that he would let nothing delay it. Nevertheless it is perfectly characteristic of him that, having now finally decided there should be no attempt at any divorce, he proceeded instantly to play with the idea again. No doubt he was being subjected to many influences of different kinds, for he sent me a letter in which he said that it seemed to be ascertained that an American divorce and remarriage would satisfy French law. If that was so, he would move heaven and earth to get all the necessary details of the procedure. He had written to a friend in Baltimore who knew all about such matters, but he implored me to find out if there were not some book which gave all possible information about the marriage and divorce laws of the separate States of North America. He asked : " Do you really think that I can go and present myself for a divorce without the knowledge of the other person ? The proceedings must be very astounding." His knowledge of America was not equal to my own, much as I had spoken to him about that country. The conduct of divorce courts in some of the United States have long ceased to astonish anybody. He told me, however, that he had actually heard of American lawyers advertising for would-be divorcers, and he prayed devoutly that he could get hold of such a man. I did my best for him on the subject, and no doubt his friend in Baltimore, of whom I know nothing, on his part sent him information. It seemed, however, that any proceeding would involve some difficulties, and on discovering this he instantly dropped the whole scheme. He wrote to me afterwards, saying : " It is probable that I leave England at the end of April. Not one syllable about me to any one, of course. The step is so bold as to be really impudent, and I often have serious fears, not, of course, on my own account. You shall hear from abroad. . . . If some day one could know tranquillity and all meet together decently."

After many qualms, hot and cold fits, despondency, and inspirations of courage, he at last took the decisive step. In May he was in Paris, and I think it was in that month that the " marriage " took place. I am singularly ignorant of the details, for he seemed to be somewhat reluctant to speak of them, and do not even know whether any actual ceremony took place or not, nor am I much concerned to know. They were at any rate together, and no doubt tolerably happy. He wrote me nothing either about this subject or anything else for some time, and I was content to hear nothing. They spent the summer together in Switzerland, moving from Trient, near the Col de Balme, to Locarno, on Lago Maggiore. He wrote to me once from the Rhône Valley saying that as a result of his new domestic peace and comfort, even though it were but the comfort of Swiss hotels, and owing to the air of the mountains, which always suited him very well, he was in much better health than he had been for years past. His lung, the perpetual subject of his preoccupation, appears to have given him little trouble, although, knowing that its state was attributable in some measure to emphysema, he wrote to me for detailed explanations of that particular complaint. During the whole of this time, the only honeymoon he ever had, he was, however, obliged to work very hard, for he was in ceaseless trouble about money. In his own words, he had to " publish furiously " in order to keep pace with his expenses. There was his wife in England, and there were also his children to be partially provided for. But for the time things went well with him. There were fears of all sorts, he told me, but they were to be forgotten as much as possible. He and Thérèse returned to Paris for the winter.

During this time, or just about this time, when the South African War was raging, I wrote for a weekly journal, which I used to send regularly to Paris with my own contributions marked in it. This temporary aberration into journalism so late in my literary life interested him much. He wrote to me : " In the old garret days who would have imagined the strange present ? I suppose you have now a very solid footing in journalism as well as in fiction. Of course it was wise to get it, as it seems more than probable that the novelists will be starved out very soon. With Europe in a state of war, which may last for a decennium, there will be little chance for story-tellers." Then, in spite of his new happiness, his inherited or acquired pessimism got the worst of him. He adds : " I wish I had died ten years ago. I should have gone away with some hope for civilisation, of which I now have none. One's choice seems to be between death in the work-house, or by some ruffian's bullet. As for those who come after one, it is too black to think about."

No doubt this was only his fun, or partly such.
There is one phrase in Boswell's "Johnson" that he
always loved to quote ; it is where Johnson declares
that some poor creature had " no skill in inebriation."
Maitland perhaps had no skill in inebriation when he
drank at the fountain of literary pessimism, for when he
did drink there his views were fantastic and preposterous. As a matter of fact he was doing very well, in
spite of the workhouse in Marylebone Road, from which
he was now far enough. There might be little chance
for story-tellers, yet his financial position, for the first
time in his life, was tolerably sound. One publisher
even gave him three hundred pounds on account for a
book which I think was " The Best of all Things." For
it he also received five hundred dollars from America ;
so, for him, or indeed for almost any writer, he was
very well paid. Little as the public may believe it,
a sum of three hundred pounds on account of royalties
is as much as any well-known man gets—unless by
chance he happens to be one of the half-dozen successful writers who are rarely the best. At my earnest
solicitation he had at last employed an agent, though,
with his peculiar readiness to receive certain impres-
sions, he had not gone to the one recommended, but to
another, suddenly mentioned to him when he was in
the mood to act as I suggested. This agent worked for
him very well, and Maitland was now getting five
guineas a thousand words for stories, which is also a
very fair price for a man who does really good work.
It is true that very bad work is not often well paid, but
the very best work of all is often not to be sold at any
price. About this time I obtained for him a notable
bid for a book, and he wrote to me : " It is good to
know that people care to make offers for my work.
What I aim at is to get a couple of thousand pounds

safely invested for my two boys. Probably I shall not succeed—and if I get the money, what security have I that it will be safe in a year or two ? As likely as not the Bank of England will lie in ruins." After all, I must confess that he was skilful in the inebriation of his pessimism, for to me these phrases are delightful, in spite of the half-belief with which they were uttered.

During the later winter of 1900 he wrote to me from Paris that he proposed to be in London for a few days in the spring of 1901, but much depended on the relation, which seemed to him highly speculative, between the money he received and the money he was obliged to spend. Apparently he found Paris anything but cheap. According to his own account, he was therefore in perpetual straits, in spite of the good prices he now obtained. He added in this letter : " I hope to speak with you once more, before we are both shot or starved." This proposal to come across the Channel in the spring ended in smoke.[1] He was not able to afford it, or was reluctant to move, or more likely reluctant to expose himself to any of the troubles still waiting for him in England. So long as his good friends who were looking after his wife, and more or less looking after his children, could do their work and save him from anxiety, he was not likely to want his peace disturbed by any discussions. When he had decided not to come he sent me a letter in which one of the paragraphs reads : " I am still trying to believe that there is a King of England, and cannot take to the idea, any more than to the moral and material ruin which seems to be coming upon the old country.

[1] Roberts' chronology at this point is inaccurate, not deliberately but because of lapse of memory. About the May of 1901 Gissing came to England, and during June and July was in the east coast sanatorium—at Nayland, Suffolk—referred to in the next chapter (see p. 199). He returned to France in August.

Isn't it astounding that we have the courage to write
books ? We shall do so, I suppose, until the day when
publishers find their business at an end. I fear it may
not be far off." At this moment, being more or less at
peace, and working with no peculiar difficulty, he
declared himself in tolerable health, although he
affirmed he coughed a great deal. It seemed to me
that he did not think so much about his health as he
had done before and was to do later, and he displayed
something like his old real nature with regard to literary
enterprise. It was just about this time that he reminded me of his cherished project for a story of the
sixth century A.D. This, of course, was the book published after his death, " Basil." He had then begun to
work upon it, and said he hoped to finish it that summer.
This cheered him up wonderfully, and he ended one
letter to me with : " Well, well, let us be glad that
again we exchange letters with address other than that
of workhouse or hospital. It is a great demand, this,
to keep sane and solvent—I dare hope for nothing
more." Occasionally in his letters there seemed to be
slight indications that he was perhaps not quite so
happy as he wished to be.

During that summer my wife and I were in Switzerland, and he wrote to me, while we were on the
Lake of Geneva, from Vernet-les-Bains in the Eastern
Pyrenees.[1] By this time Thérèse and I, although we
had never met, were accustomed to send messages to each
other. It was a comfort to me to feel that he was with
some one of whom I could think pleasantly, and whom
I much wished to know. We had, indeed, arranged to
meet somewhere on the Continent, but that fell through,
partly because we were obliged to return to England

[1] Gissing, on his return to France in August 1901, went first to Autun ; then
to Tazières during part of October and November ; and in December he went to
winter at Arcachon.

earlier than we had proposed. Although we did not meet, and though I had some fears for him, I was tolerably happy about him and his affairs, and certainly did not anticipate the new crisis which was approaching, nor the form it would take.

# XI

IT was Maitland's custom to rely for advice and assistance on particular people at certain crises. In some cases he now appealed to Rivers ; in very many he appealed to me ; but when his health was particularly involved it was his custom to relapse desperately on his friend Dr. Lake. He even came to Lake on his return from Magna Græcia, when he had taken Potsdam on his way home to England.[1] He had gone there at Schmidt's strong invitation and particular desire that he should taste for once a real Westphalian ham. It is a peculiarly savage and not wholly safe custom of Germans to eat such hams uncooked, and Maitland, having fallen in with this custom, though he escaped trichinosis, procured for himself a peculiarly severe attack of indigestion. He came over from Folkestone to Lake in order to get cured. The ham apparently had not given him the lasting satisfaction which he usually got out of fine fat feeding. It seems that Lake and Maitland had been friends from the time that Maitland's father bought his chemist's business from the doctor's father. For they had been schoolfellows together at Hinkson's school in Mirefields. Nevertheless it was only in 1894 that they renewed their old acquaintance. Dr. Lake saw him once at Ewell, soon after a local practioner had frightened Maitland very seriously by diagnosing phthisis and giving a gloomy prognosis. On that occasion Lake went over Maitland's chest and found very little wrong. Technically speaking, there was perhaps a slight want of

[1] In the late spring of 1898.

expansion at the apex of each lung, and apparently some emphysema at the base of the left one, but certainly no active tubercular mischief.

I speak of these things more or less in detail because health played so great a part in the drama of his life ; as, indeed, it does in most lives. It is not the casual thing that novelists mostly make of it. It is a perpetually acting cause. Steady ill-health, even more than actually acute disease, is what helps to bring about most tragedies. When Lake made his diagnosis, with which I agree, though there is something else I must presently add to it, he took him to London, that he might see a notable physician, in order to reassure Maitland's mind thoroughly. They went together to Dr. Prior Smithson. I have never noted that it was Maitland who introduced Dr. Lake to Rivers.[1] When Lake had arranged this London visit Maitland wrote to Rivers saying : " I am coming up to town to see a scoundrel specialist in diseases of the lung, who is as likely as not to upset all my plans of life. But don't be afraid of my company ; you shall have no pathology. There will be with me an old schoolfellow of mine, a country surgeon, in whose house I am staying at present. He would think it very delightful to meet you." They did meet upon that occasion, when Dr. Smithson confirmed Lake's diagnosis and temporarily did a great deal to comfort Maitland. From my own medical knowledge and my general study of Maitland, combined with what some of his doctors have told me, I have come to the conclusion that he did suffer from pulmonary tuberculosis, but that it was practically arrested at an early stage. However, even arrested tuberculosis in many cases leaves a very poor state of nutrition. That his joy in

[1] Wells and Gissing had first met in November 1896. Hick later became Wells's doctor at Sandgate.

food remained with him, though with a few lapses, points strongly to the conclusion that at this time tuberculosis was certainly not very active in him. He always needed much food, and especially food which he liked and desired. To want it was a tragedy, as I shall show presently.

In 1897 when he went down to Salcombe he reported to Lake a great improvement in health, saying that his cough was practically gone, and that of course the wonderful weather accounted for it. He ate heartily and even walked five miles a day without fatigue. He added : " The only difficulty is breathing through the nose. The other day a traction engine passed me on the road, and the men upon it looked about them wondering where the strange noises came from. It was my snoring ! All the nasal cavities are excoriated ! But I shall get used to this. I have a suspicion that it is *not* the lung that accounts for this difficulty, for it has been the same ever since I can remember." By this he probably meant merely that it had lasted a long time. There was, perhaps, a specific reason for it. From Salcombe he reported to Lake that he had recovered a great deal of weight, but that for some time his wheezing had been worse than ever when the weather got very bad. He wrote : " Then again a practical paradox that frenzies one, for sleep came when bad weather prevented me from being so much out of doors ! " All this he did not understand, but it is highly probable that at that time he had a little actual tubercular mischief, and a slight rise of temperature. As frequently happens, enforced rest in the house did for him what nothing else could do. But his health certainly was something of a puzzle. In 1898,[1] when he was in Paris with Thérèse, he saw a Dr. Piffard,

[1] 1899, at the earliest.

apparently not a lung specialist, but a physician of high standing. This doctor spoke rather gravely to him, and told him that he was working very much too hard, for he was still keeping up his ridiculous habit of writing eight hours a day. He said that there was a moist spot in the right lung, with a little chronic bronchitis, and that the emphysema was very obvious. He had, too, some chronic rheumatism, and also on the right side of his forehead what Maitland described as a patch of psoriasis. Psoriasis, however, is not as a rule unilateral, and it was due to something else. This patch had been there for about a year, and was slowly getting worse. Dr. Piffard prescribed touching him under the right clavicle with the actual cautery, and for the skin gave him some subcutaneous injections of an arsenical preparation. He fed him with eggs, milk, and cod-liver oil, ordering much sleep and absolute rest. During this treatment he improved somewhat, and owned that he felt really better. The cough had become trifling, his breathing was easier, and his sleep very good. His strength had much increased. He also declared that he saw a slight amelioration in the patch of so-called psoriasis. The truth is, I think, that nearly all this improvement was due to his being made to rest and eat. No doubt very much of his ill-health was the result of his abnormal habits, although there was something else at the back of it. For one thing he had rarely taken sufficient exercise, the exercise necessary for his really fine physique. Certainly he never played a game in his life after he left Hinkson's school in Mirefields. Cricket he knew not. Football was a mystery to him, and a brutal mystery at that. It is true that occasionally he rowed in a boat at the seaside, for he did so at Salcombe when his eldest boy was there with him, but any kind of game or sport he actually loathed.

It was a surprise to me to find out that Rivers, while he was at Folkestone,[1] actually persuaded him to take to a bicycle. He even learned to like it. Rivers told Lake that he rode not badly, and with great dignity ; and as Rivers rode beside him he heard him murmur : " Marvellous proceedings ! Was the like ever seen ? "

However, the time was now coming when he was to appeal to Lake once more. In 1901 he had proposed to come over to England and see me, but he said that the doctor in Paris had forbidden him to go north, rather indicating the south for him. He wrote to me : " Now I must go to the centre of France—I don't think the Alps are possible—and vegetate among things which serve only to remind me that here is *not* England. Then, again, I had thought night and day of an English potato, of a slice of English meat, of tarts and puddings, and of teacakes. Night and day had I looked forward to ravening on these things. Well, well ! " But he did at last come back to England for some time.

There is no doubt that the feeding in his French home was not fat, or fine, or confused feeding. Probably the notion of a Scotch haggis would give any French cook a fit of apoplexy. Just before he did come over from Paris, Lake had a letter from him which was much like the one he wrote to me : " Best wishes for the merry, merry time—if merriment can be in the evil England of these days. I wish I could look in upon you at Christmas. I should roar with joy at an honest bit of English roast beef. Could you post a slice in a letter ?—with gravy ? " Lake said to his wife when he received this letter : " Why, this is written by a starving man ! " Although I heard from him comparatively seldom, I had always been aware of these hankerings of his for England and English food. He did not take

[1] Sandgate.

kindly to exile, or to the culinary methods of a careful French interior. Truly as he loved the Latin countries, there was much in their customs which troubled him greatly, and the food was his especial trouble when he was not being fed in Italy with oil and Chianti. I find occasional melancholy letters of his in which he indulged in dithyrambs about the fine abundance of feeding in England—eggs and bacon and beer. There was no doubt he was not living as he should have lived. At any rate, it was about this time—although I did not know it, as I was either in the North of England or abroad, I forget which—that he came once more to Lake, and was found standing on his doorstep tolerably early in the morning.[1] According to the doctor, on his arrival from Paris he was in the condition of a starved man. The proof of this is very simple. At that time, and for long after, Rivers was living at Folkestone, and as Lake's house was at that time full he was unable to entertain Maitland for long, and it was proposed that he should stay for a time at Folkestone. When Lake examined Maitland he was practically no more than a skeleton, but after one week in Rivers' house he picked up no less than seven pounds weight. There were then no physical signs of active mischief in the lungs except the incurable patch of emphysema. Although this sudden increase of weight does not entirely exclude tuberculosis, it is yet rather uncommon for so rapid an increase to take place in such cases, and it rather puts tuberculosis out of court as being in any way the real cause of much of his ill-health. Now of all this I knew very little, or next to nothing, until afterwards. Although aware that he was uneasy about many things, I had not gathered that there was anything

[1] This seems to be an error. It was when he first left his wife that he was found on Lake's doorstep. On this occasion he went first to Folkestone : Lake as asked to come and see him. (R.) This was about May 1901.

seriously wrong with him except his strong and almost irresistible desire to return to England. I know now that his reticence in speaking to me was due to his utter inability to confess that his third venture had almost come to disaster over the mere matter of the dining-table. I knew so much of the past that he feared to tell me of the present, though he could hardly have imagined that I should say anything to make him feel that he had once again been a sad fool for not insisting good-humouredly on having the food he wanted. But he was ashamed to speak to me of his difficulties, fearing, perhaps, that I might not understand, or understand too well.

Now he and Thérèse lived together with Madame Espinel. The old lady, a very admirable and delicate creature of an aristocratic type, was no longer young, and was typically French. She was in a poor state of health, and lived, like Cornaro, on next to nothing. Her views on food were what Maitland would have described as highly exiguous. She stood bravely by the French breakfast, a thing Maitland could endure with comfort for no more than a week or two at a time. Her notions as to the midday meal and dinner were not characterised by that early English abundance which he so ardently desired. After a long period of subdued friction on the subject it appears that his endurance of what he called prolonged starvation actually broke down. He demanded something for breakfast, something fat, something in the nature of bacon. How this was procured I do not know ; I presume that bacon can be bought in Paris, though I do not remember having seen it there ; perhaps it was imported from England for his especial benefit. However pleasing for the moment the result may have been to him from the gastronomic point of view, it led Madame Espinel to make, as he alleged, uncalled-for and bitter remarks upon the English grossness of his tastes. As he was certainly run down and much underfed, his nerves were starved too, so he got into one of his sudden rages and practically ran away from France. I suggested not long ago that he was in a way an intellectual coward because he would never entertain any question as to the nature of the universe, or of our human existence in it. Things were to be taken as they stood, and not examined, for fear of pain or mental disturbance. It was a little later than this that Rivers said acutely to Lake : " Why, the man is a moral coward. He stands things up to a certain point and then runs away." So now he ran away from French feeding to Lake's doorstep, and Lake, as I have said, sent him to Rivers with the very best results, for Mrs. Rivers took a great interest in him, looking on him no doubt as a kind of foolish child of genius, and fed him, by Lake's direction, for all that she was worth. As soon as he was in anything like condition, or getting towards it, he was unable to remain any longer at Folkestone and proposed to return once more to France. This, however, the doctor forbade, and, thinking that a prolonged course of feeding and rest was the one thing he required, induced him to go to a sanatorium in the east of England.[1] At this time Lake had practically no belief whatever in the man being tuberculous, but he used Maitland's firm conviction that he was in that condition to induce him to enter this establishment. It was perhaps the best thing which could be done for him. He was looked after very well, and the doctor at the sanatorium agreed with Lake in finding no evidence of active pulmonary trouble.

Maitland kept much, or most, of this from me—it

[1] See note to p. 189.

was very natural. He wrote to me from the sanatorium very many letters, from which I shall not quote, as they were after all only the natural moans of a solitary invalid. But he forbade me to come to him, and I did not insist on paying a visit. I was quite aware, if it were only by instinct and intuition, that he had no desire for me to discover exactly how things had been going with him in France. Nevertheless I did understand vaguely, though it was not till afterwards that I discovered there had been a suggestion made that he should not return there, or, indeed, go back to the circumstances which had proved so nearly disastrous. I do not think that this suggestion was ever made personally to him, although I understand it was discussed by some of his friends. It appears that a year or so afterwards when he was talking to Miss Kingdon, she told him that it had been thought possible that he might not return to France. This news he received with much amazement and indignation, for certainly he did go back, and henceforth I believe the management of the kitchen was conducted on more reasonable lines. He recovered his normal weight, and soon weighed actually twelve stone. As a matter of fact, even before he left the sanatorium, he protested that he was actually getting obese.

After these experiences at Folkestone and the east of England, he was perfectly conscious that he owed very much both to Lake and Rivers. In fact he wrote to the doctor afterwards, saying that he and Rivers had picked him out of a very swampy place.

It was in 1902 that Maitland and Thérèse took up their abode in St. Pé d'Ascain,[1] under the Pyrenees. From there he wrote to me very frequently, and seemed

[1] St. Jean-de-Luz. First, from April 24, at the Pension Larréa ; and later, about July, in a furnished villa at Ciboure.

to be doing a great deal of work. He liked the place, and, as there was an English colony in the town, had made not a few friends or acquaintances. By now it was a very long time since I had seen him, for we had not met during the time of his illness in England ; and as I had been much overworked, it occurred to me that three or four days at sea might do something for me, and that I could combine this with a visit to my old friend. I did not, however, write to him that I was coming. Knowing his ways and his peculiar nervousness, which at this time most visibly grew upon him, it seemed best to say nothing until I actually came to Bordeaux. When I reached the city on the Gironde I telegraphed to know whether he could receive me. The answer was one word only, " Venez," and I went down by the early train, through the melancholy Landes, and came at last to St. Pé by way of Bayonne. He met me at the station—which, by the way, has one of the most beautiful views I know—and I found him looking almost exactly as he had looked before, save that he arranged his hair for the time to hide a fading scar upon his forehead, the result of that mysterious skin trouble. We were, I know, very glad to meet.

I stayed at a little hotel by myself as he could not put me up, but went later to his house. It was then that I at last met Thérèse. She was a very beautiful woman, tall and slender, of a pale but clear complexion, very melancholy lovely eyes, and a voice that was absolute music. I could not help thinking that he had at last come home, for at that time my knowledge of their little domestic difficulties owing to the warring customs of their different countries was very vague, and she impressed me greatly. And yet I knew before I left that night that all was not well with Maitland, though it seemed so well with him. He complained to me when we were alone about his health, and even then protested somewhat forcibly against the meals. The house itself, or their apartment—from the foreign point of view—was quite comfortable, but did not suggest the kind of surroundings which Maitland loved. There is, save in the best, a certain air of cold barrenness about so many foreign houses. The absence of rugs or carpets and curtains, the polish and exiguity of the furniture, the general air of having no more in the rooms than that which will just serve the purposes of life did not suit his sense of abundance and luxury.

Blake has said, if I quote with accuracy : " We do not know that we have enough until we have had too much," and this is a saying of wisdom as well concerning the things of the mind as those of the body. He had had at last a little too much domesticity, and, besides that, his desires were set towards London and the British Museum, with possibly half the year spent in Devonshire. He yearned to get away from the little polished French home he had made for himself and take Thérèse back to England with him. But this was impossible, for her mother still lived with them and naturally would not consent to expatriate herself at her age from her beloved France. It had been truly no little sacrifice for her, a very gentle and delicate woman even then suffering from cardiac trouble, to leave Paris and its neighbourhood and stay with her child near the frontier of Spain, almost beyond the borders of French civilisation.

I was barely a week in St. Pé d'Ascain, but during that time we talked much both of his work and of mine. Once more his romance of the sixth century was in his mind and on his desk, though he worked more, perhaps, at necessary pot-boilers than at this long pondered task.

Although he did not write so much as of old, it was almost impossible to get him to go out with me, save now and again for half an hour in the warmest and quietest part of the day. He had developed a great fear of death, and life seemed to him extraordinarily fragile. Such a feeling is ever the greatest warning to those who know, and yet if he had been rather more courageous and had faced the weather a little more, it might have been better for him. During these few days I became very friendly with Madame Espinel and her daughter, but more especially with the latter, because she spoke English, and my French has never been fluent. As I went away he gave me a copy of his new book, " The Meditations of Mark Sumner." It is one of those odd things which occur so frequently in literary life that I had myself in a way given him the notion of this book. I had developed the idea of such a book to him upon my own account, when I purposed vaguely to write a short life of an imaginary man of letters to whom I meant to attribute what I afterwards published in " Apteryx." [1] Perhaps this seed had lain dormant in Maitland's mind for years, and when at last he wrote the book he had wholly forgotten that it was I who first suggested the idea. Certainly no two books could have been more different, although my own plan was originally much more like his. In the same way I now believe that my story " The Purification " owed its inception without my being aware of it to the suppressed passage in " Outside the Pale " of which I spoke some time ago. This passage I never read ; but, when Maitland told me of it, it struck me greatly and remained in my mind. These influences are one of the great uses of companionship among men of letters. As Henry Maitland used to say : " We come together and strike out sparks."

[1] Possibly *Albany*. See note to p. 234.

As I went north by train from St. Pé d'Ascain to
Bordeaux, passing ancient Dax and all the sombre
silences of the wounded serried rows of pines which have
made an infertile soil yield something to commerce,
Maitland's spirit, his wounded and often sickly spirit,
was with me. I say " sickly " with a certain reluctance,
and yet that is what I felt, for I read " The Meditations "
with great revolt in spite of its obvious beauty and literary
sincerity. Life is hard and bitter enough to break any
man's spirit, and I felt that Maitland had been through
a fire not many men had known, yet as I read I thought,
and still think, that in this book he showed an undue
failure of courage. If he had been through so many
disasters yet there was still much left for him, or should
have been. He had not suffered the greatest disaster
of all, for since the death of his father in his early
youth he had lost none that he loved. The calculated
dispirited air of the book afflicted me, and yet, naturally
enough, I found it wonderfully interesting ; for here
was so much of my lifelong friend, even though now and
again there were little lapses in sincerity when he put
another face on things, and pretended, even to himself,
that he had felt in one way and not in another. There
is in it only a brief mention of myself,[1] when he refers to
the one solitary friend he possessed in London through so
many years which were only not barren to him in the
acquisition of knowledge.

But even as I read in the falling night I came to the
passage [2] in which he speaks of the Anabasis. It is
curious to think of, but I doubt if he had ever heard that
some modern scholars refuse to believe that Xenophon
wrote this book. Most assuredly had he heard it he
would have rejected so revolutionary a notion with rage
and indignation, for to him Xenophon and the Anabasis

[1] *Henry Ryecroft :* " Spring," VIII.  [2] *Ibid. :* " Summer," IX.

were one. In speaking of the march of the Greeks he quotes the passage where they rewarded and dismissed the guide who had led them through very dangerous country. The text says : " When evening came he took leave of us, and went his way by night." On reaching Bordeaux I surprised and troubled the telegraph clerk at the railway station by telegraphing to Henry Maitland those words in the original Greek, though naturally I had to write them in common script. Often-times I had been his guide but had never led him in safety.

When I reached England I wrote him a very long letter about " The Meditations," and in answer received one which I may here quote : " My dear old boy, it is right and good that the first word about ' Mark Sumner ' should come from you. I am delighted that you find it readable. For a good ten years I had this book in mind vaguely, and for two years have been getting it into shape. You will find that there is not very much reminiscence ; more philosophising. Why, of course, the solitary friend is you. Good old Schmidt is mentioned later. But the thing is a curious blend, of course, of truth and fiction. Why, it's just because the world is ' inexplicable ' that I feel my interest in it and its future grows less and less. I am a little oppressed by ' the burden of the mystery ' ; not seldom I think with deep content of the time when speculation will be at an end. But my delight in the beauty of the visible world, and my enjoyment of the great things of literature, grow stronger. My one desire now is to *utter* this passion—yet the result of one's attempt is rather a poor culmination for Life."

During this year, and indeed during the greater part of 1902, I was very ill and much troubled, though I worked hard upon my longest book, " Rachel." [1]    I

[1] *Rachel Marr* (1903).

therefore wrote to him very seldom until, in the beginning of the following spring, I was able to send him the book. I was conscious through all my working years that I had never actually conquered Maitland's utmost approval. For I knew what his enthusiasm was when he was really roused ; how obvious, how sincere, and how tremendous. When reflecting that I did at last conquer it just before he died I have a certain melancholy pleasure in that book of mine, which indeed in many ways means very much to me, much more than I can put down, or would put down for any one now living. Were I now doing a life of myself rather than a sketch of him, I should certainly put in the letter, knowing that I should be forgiven for inserting it because it was a letter of Maitland's. It was, indeed, a highly characteristic epistle, for when he praised he praised indeed, and his words carried conviction to me, ever somewhat sceptical of most men's approval. He did even more than write to me, for I learnt that he spoke about this book to other friends of his, especially, as I know, to Edmund Roden ; and also to George Meredith, who talked to me about it with satisfaction when I next met him. Nothing pleased Maitland better than that any one he loved should do good work. If ever a man lived who was free from the prevalent vices of artistic and literary jealousy, it was Maitland.

But now his time was drawing to an end. He and Thérèse and Madame Espinel left St. Pé d'Ascain in June, 1903, and went thirty miles farther into the Pyrenees. He wrote to me a few days after reaching the little mountain town of St. Christophe.[1] The change apparently did him good. He declared that he had now no more sciatica, of which disease, by the way, I had not previously heard, and he admitted that his

[1] St. Jean-Pied-de-Port : " Ispoure " was the address.

general health was improving. St. Christophe is very
picturesquely situated, and Maitland loved it not the
less for its associations in ancient legend, since it is not
very far from the Port or Col de Roncesvalles, where
the legendary Roland was slain fighting in the rear-
guard to protect Charlemagne's army. He and Thérèse
once stayed a night at Roncesvalles. If any man's live
imagination heard the horn of Roland blow I think it
should be Maitland's. And yet though he took a great
pleasure in this country of his, it was not England, nor
had he all things at his command which he desired. I
find that he now greatly missed the British Museum,
which readers of " The Meditations " will know he much
frequented in those old days. For he was once more
hard at work upon " Basil," and wrote to me that he
was greatly in want of exact knowledge about the procedure in the execution of wills under the later Roman
Empire. This was a request for information, and such
requests I not infrequently received. He often referred
to me about points of difficulty, even when he was in
England but away from London. At that time, naturally enough, I knew nothing whatever about wills under
the Roman Empire, but in less than a week after he had
written to me it is highly probable that I knew more
of them than any lawyer in London who was not actually
lecturing on the subject. I sent him a long screed on
the matter. Before this reached him I got another letter
giving me more details of what he required, and, since
this is certainly of some interest as showing his literary
methods and conscientiousness, it may be quoted. He
says : " And now, hearty thanks for troubling about
the legal question. The time with which I am concerned is about A.D. 540. I know, of course, that de-
generation and the Gothic War made semi-chaos of
Roman civilisation ; but as a matter of fact the Roman

law still existed. The Goths never interfered with it,
and portions have even been handed down. Now the
testator is a senator. He has one child only, a daughter,
and to her leaves most of his estate. There are legacies
to two nephews, and to a sister. A very simple will,
you see—no difficulty about it. But he dying, all
the legatees being with him at the time, how, as a
matter of fact, were things settled ? Was an executor
appointed ? Might an executor be a legatee ? Probate,
I think, as you say, there was none, but who inherited ?
Still fantastic things were done in those times, but what
would the law have dictated ? Funny, too, that this
is the only real difficulty which bothers me in the course
of my story. As regards all else that enters into the
book I believe I know as much as one can without being
a Mommsen. The senator owns property in Rome and
elsewhere. I rather suppose it was a case of taking
possession if you could, and holding if no one interfered
with you. Wills of this date were frequently set aside
on the mere assertion of a powerful senator that the
testator had verbally expressed a wish to benefit him. . . .
It is a glorious age for a romancer." As a full answer
to this letter I borrowed and sent to him Saunders'
" Justinian," and received typically exaggerated thanks.

# XII

NOW again we were but correspondents, and I do not think that in those days when I had so much to do, and had also very bad health, I was a good correspondent. Maitland, although he sometimes apologised humorously, even nervously, for writing at great length, was an admirable letter writer. He practised a lost art, which he admired in Chesterfield and Madame de Sevigné, and often drew sharply etched portraits of people whom he knew at St. Pé. He had a curious habit of nicknaming everybody. These nicknames were perhaps not the highest form of art, nor were they always even humorous. He had a peculiarly verbal humour in these matters. Never by any chance, unless he was exceedingly serious, did he call any man by his actual name. Hudson,[1] my lifelong friend, whom he knew very well, and whose books he admired very much for their style, was always known as " The Hudsonian," and I was referred to by a similarly formed name. To the three of us who met together wherever we could there was presently joined an artist,[2] happily still living, and it was Maitland's jest to name us " the Quadrilateral " after the four fortresses of Lombardy : Mantua, Peschiera, Verona, and Legnano. Which of us represented the master power of Mantua remained undetermined. These are matters of no consequence, but they show the man in his familiar moods and therefore have a kind of value— as if one were to show a score of photographs or sketches that were serious and then insert one where the wise

[1] W. H. Hudson (1841–1922).    [2] Alfred Hartley (1855–1933).

man plays the child, or even the fool. There was not a person of any importance in St. Pé d'Ascain, although nobody knew it, who did not rejoice in some absurd nickname.

However he went further than mere nicknames, and there is in one letter of his to Rivers a very admirable sketch of a certain personage : " One of the most cantankerous men I ever came across ; fierce against the modern tendencies of science, especially in England : an anti-Darwinite, etc. He rages against Huxley, accusing him of having used his position for personal vanity and gain, and of ruining the scientific and industrial prospects of England ; charges of the paltriest dishonesty against H. and other such men abound in his conversation. X., it seems, was one of the original students of the Jermyn Street School of Mines, and his root grievance is the transformation of that establishment—brought about, he declares, for the personal profit of Huxley and of—the clerks of the War Office ! *You*, he regards as a most valuable demonstration of the evils resulting from the last half-century of ' progress,' protesting loudly that every one of your books is a bitter satire on Huxley, his congeners, and his disciples. The man tells me that no scientific papers in England will print his writing, merely from personal enmity. He has also quarrelled with the scientific societies of France, and now, being a polyglot, he writes for Spain and Germany—the only two countries in Europe where scientific impartiality is to be found."

In another letter of his he says : " By the bye, an English paper states that Henley died worth something more than eight hundred pounds." One might imagine that he would then proceed to condole with him on having had so little to leave, but that was not our Maitland. He went on : "Amazing ! How on earth did he amass that wealth ? I am rejoiced to know that his latter years have been passed without struggle for bread."

The long letter about the Roman Empire and Roman law, from which I quoted in the last chapter, was dated August 6, 1903, and I did not hear again from Maitland until November 1. I had written to him proposing to pay another visit to the south-west of France in order to see him in his Pyrenean home, but he replied very gloomily, saying that he was in evil case, that Thérèse had laryngitis, and that everything was made worse by incredibly bad weather. The workhouse—still the workhouse—was staring him in the face. He had to labour a certain number of hours each day in direly unfavourable conditions. If he did not finish his book at the end of the year sheer pauperdom would come upon him. In these circumstances I was to see that he dreaded a visit from any friend, indeed he was afraid that they would not be able to stay in St. Christophe on account of its excessive dampness. According to this pathetically exaggerated account they lived in a thick mist day and night. How on earth it came to be thought that such a dreadful country was good for consumptive people he could not imagine ; though he owned, somewhat grudgingly, that he himself had gained strength there. He told me that as soon as the eternal downpour ceased they were going down to Bayonne to see a doctor, and if he did no good Thérèse would go to the south of France. Finally, he was hanged if he knew how it would be managed. He ended up with : " In short I have not often in my life been nearer to an appalling crisis." At the end of this dismal letter, which did not affect me so much as might be thought, he spoke to me of my book, " Rachel," and said : " I have been turning the pages with great pleasure to keep my thoughts from the workhouse."

Those will have gathered very little of Maitland who imagine that I took this *au pied de la lettre*. Maitland had cried " Wolf ! " so often, that I had almost ceased to believe that there were wolves, even in the Pyrenees. All things had gradually become appalling crises and dreadful disasters. A mere disturbance and an actual catastrophe were alike dire and irremediable calamities. And yet, alas, there was more truth underlying his words than even he knew. If a man lives for ever in shadow the hour arrives at last when there is no more light ; and even for those who look forward, one would think with a certain relief, to the workhouse, there comes a day when they shall work no more. I smiled when I read this letter, but, of course, telegraphed to him deferring my visit until the rain had ceased, or laryngitis had departed from his house, or until his spirits recovered their tone on the completion of his great romance. One could do no other, much as I desired to see him and have one of our prodigious and preposterously long talks in his new home. I do not think that I wrote to him after this lamentable reply of his, but on November 16 I received my last communication from him. It was three lines on a postcard, still dated from St. Christophe. He referred in it once more to my book, and said : " Delighted to see the advertisement in —— to-day, especially after their very base notice last week. Hurrah! Illness and struggle still going on here." The struggle I believed in, but, as ever with one's friends, one doubted if the illness were serious. And yet the catastrophe was coming.

At this time I was myself seriously ill, and had been in bed for nearly a fortnight. During the early days of my convalescence I went to my club, and got this telegram from Rivers : " Have received following telegram from Maitland, ' Henry dying. Entreat you

to come. In greatest haste.' I cannot go, can you ? "
This message to me was dated Folkestone, where Rivers
was then living. Now at this time I was feeling utterly
unfit to travel. I hardly knew what to do, but thought
it best to go home and consult with my wife before
replying to Rivers. Anxious as she was to do everything
possible for Maitland, she implored me not to venture
on so long a journey, especially as it was in mid-winter,
just at Christmas-time. If I had not felt really ill she
would not have placed any obstacles in my path. She
would, indeed, have urged me to go. After a little
reflection I therefore replied to Rivers [1] that I was myself
very ill, but added that if he really could not go I would.
At the same time I telegraphed to Maitland, or rather to
Thérèse, saying that I was ill, but would come if she
found it absolutely necessary. I do not think I received
any answer to this message, a fact one easily understands
when one learns how desperate things really were ; but
on December 26 I had another telegram from Rivers,
and found that he had gone to St. Christophe in spite
of not being well.[2] He wired to me : " No nurse.
Nursing help may save Maitland. Come if possibly
can. Am here but ill." Such an appeal could not be
resisted. If Rivers was ill at St. Christophe it now
seemed my absolute duty to go, whatever my own state
of health.

I left London that night by the last train, crossing
to Paris by way of Newhaven and Dieppe in order to
get at least three hours of rest in a recumbent position
in the steamer, as I did not at that time feel justified in
going all the way first class and taking a sleeper. I did
manage to obtain some rest during the sea-passage, but
on reaching Paris early in the morning I felt exceedingly

[1] Wells, according to his account of the matter, did not receive this reply before
he set out.　　　　　　　　　　[2] He had left England on Christmas Eve.

unwell, and at the Gare St. Lazare found at that hour
no means of obtaining even a cup of coffee. I drove over
to the Quai d'Orsay, and spent an hour or two in the
coffee-room waiting for the departure of the express to
Bordeaux. Ill as I was, and full of anxiety about
Maitland, and now about Rivers, that journey was one
long nightmare. I had not been able to take the Sud
Express, and when at last, late in the evening, I reached
Bayonne, I found that the last train to St. Christophe
in its high Pyrenean valley had already gone hours
before my arrival. While on my journey I had again
telegraphed from Morcenx to Rivers or to Thérèse
asking them to telegraph to me at the Hôtel du Commerce, Bayonne, in case I was unable to get on that
night, as I had indeed feared, although I was unable to
get accurate information. On reaching this hotel I
found waiting for me a telegram, which I have now
lost, that was somehow exceedingly obscure but yet
portended disaster. That I expected the worst I know,
for I telegraphed to my wife the news in code that
Maitland was dying and that the doctor gave no
hope.

If I had been a rich man, or even moderately furnished
with money on that journey, I should have taken a
motor-car if it could have been obtained, and have gone
on at once without waiting for the morning. But now
I was obliged to spend the night in that little old-fashioned
hotel in the old English city of Bayonne, the city whose
fortress bears the proud emblem " Nunquam polluta."
I wondered much if I should yet see my old friend alive.
It was possible, and I hoped. At any rate, he must
know that I was coming and was near at hand if only
he were yet conscious. How much I was needed I did
not know till afterwards, for even as I was going south
Rivers was once more returning to Paris on his home-

ward journey.[1] As I learnt afterwards, he was far too unwell to stay. In the morning I took the first train to St. Christophe, passing Cambo, where Rostand, the poet, makes his home. On reaching the town where Maitland lived I found no one waiting for me, though, naturally enough, I thought it possible that unless Rivers were very ill he would be able to meet me. It was a cold and gloomy morning when I left the station, and hired a small boy to show me the house in which Maitland lived on the outskirts of the little Pyrenean town. This house, it seems, was let in flats, and the Maitlands occupied the first floor. On entering the hall I found a servant washing down the stone flooring. I said to her, " Comment Monsieur se porte-t-il ? " and she replied, " Monsieur est mort." I then asked her where I should find the other Englishman. She answered that he had gone back to England the day before, and then took me upstairs and went in to tell Thérèse that I had come.

I found her with her mother. She was the only woman who had given him any happiness. Now she was completely broken down by the anxiety and distress which had come upon her so suddenly. For indeed it seems that it had been sudden. Only four or five days ago Maitland had been working hard upon " Basil," the book from which he hoped so much, and in which he believed so fervently. Then it seems that he developed what he called a cold, some slight affection of the lungs which raised his temperature a little. Strangely enough he did not take the care of himself that he should have taken, or the care which one might have expected him to take, considering his curiously expressed nervousness about himself. By some odd fatality he became suddenly

---

[1] Gissing died early on the morning of Monday, December 28, 1903. Wells had left the previous afternoon, in the expectation that Roberts was arriving that evening. As we are here told, he was unable to arrive until the next morning, too late to find his friend alive.

courageous at the wrong time, and went out for a walk
in desperately bad weather.   On the following day he
was obviously very ill, and sent for the doctor, who
suspended judgment but feared that he had pneumonia.
On the day succeeding this another doctor was called
into consultation, and the diagnosis of pneumonia was
confirmed without any doubt.   But that was not,
perhaps, what actually killed him.   There was a very
serious complication, according to Maitland's first
physician, with whom I afterwards had a long conversation, partly through the intermediary of the nurse,
an Englishwoman from Bayonne, who talked French
more fluently than myself.   He considered that Maitland
also had myocarditis.   I certainly did not think, and
do not think, that he was right in this.   Myocarditis is
rarely accompanied with much or severe pain, while the
anguish of violent pericarditis is often very great, and
Maitland had suffered most atrociously.   He was not
now a strong man, not one with big reserves and powers
of passive endurance, and in his agony he cried aloud
for death.

In these agonies there were periods of comparative
ease when he rested and was quiet, and even spoke a
little.   In one of these intermissions Thérèse came to him
and told him that I was now actually on my way.
There is no reason, I think, why I should not write what
he said.   It was simply, " Good old H——." [1]   By this
time Rivers had gone ; but before his departure he had,
I understand, procured the nurse.   The last struggle
came early that morning, December 28, while I was at
the Bayonne hotel preparing to catch the early train.
He died quietly just before dawn, I think at six o'clock.

I was taken in to see Thérèse, who was still in bed,
and found her mother with her.   They were two desolate

[1] R—— (*i.e.* Roberts).

and lonely women, and I had some fears that Thérèse would hardly recover from the blow, so deeply did his death affect her. She was always a delicate woman, and came from a delicate, neurotic stock, as one could see so plainly in the elder woman. I did my best to say what one could say, though all that can possibly be said in such cases is nothing after all. There is no physic for grief but the slow, inevitable years. I stayed not long, but went into the other chamber and saw my dead friend. The bed on which he lay stood in a little alcove at the end of the room farthest from the window.[1] He looked strangely and peculiarly intellectual, as so often happens after death. The final relaxation of the muscles about his chin and mouth accentuated most markedly the strong form of his skull. Curiously enough, as he had grown a little beard in his last illness, it seemed to me that he resembled very strongly another English writer not yet dead, one whom nature had, indeed, marked out as a story-teller, but who lacked all those qualities which made Maitland what he was. As I stood by this death-bed knowing that he had died at last in the strange anguish which he had feared, it seemed to me that here was a man who had been born to inherit grief. He had never known pure peace or utter joy as some even of the very humblest know them. I looked back across the toilsome path by which he had come hither to the end, and it seemed to me that from the very first he had been doomed. In other times or some other age he might have had a better fate, but he was born out of his time and died in exile doubly. I put my hand upon his forehead and said farewell to him and left the room, for I knew that there was much to do and that I had to do it.

[1] Here, in the first edition, follows the sentence : " I remember that the nurse, who behaved most considerately to me, stood by the window while I said farewell to him."

Thérèse was most anxious that he should not be buried in St. Christophe, of which she had conceived a natural horror. There was at this time an English clergyman in the village, the chaplain of the English church at St. Pé,[1] about whom I shall have something to say later. With him I concerted what was to be done, and he obtained the necessary papers from the *mairie*. And all this time, across the road from the stone house in which Henry Maitland lay dead, I heard the sound of his coffin being made in the little carpenter's shop which stood there. When all was done that could be done, and everything was in order, I went to the little hotel and had my lunch alone, and afterwards dined alone and slept that night in the same hotel. The next day, late in the afternoon, I went down to St. Pé d'Ascain in charge of his body. During this journey the young doctor [2] who had attended Maitland accompanied me part of the way, and for the rest of it his nurse was my companion. At St. Pé d'Ascain, where it was then quite dark, we were received by the clergyman, who had preceded us, and by a hearse, into which we carried Maitland's body. I accompanied it to the English chapel, where it remained all night before the altar. I slept at my old hotel, where I was known, as I had stayed there at the time I last saw Maitland alive.

In the morning a service was held for him according to the rites of the English Church. This was the desire of Thérèse and Madame Espinel, who, if it had been possible, would have desired to bury him according to the rites of the Catholic Church. Maitland, of course, had no orthodox belief. He refused to think of these things, for they were disturbing and led nowhither. Attending this service there were many English people, some who knew him, and some again who did not know

---

[1] The Rev. Theodore Cooper.    [2] Dr. Malpas of Biarritz.

him but went there out of respect for his name and reputation, and perhaps because they felt that they and he were alike in exile. We buried him in the common cemetery of St. Pé, a place not unbeautiful, nor unbeautifully situated. And while the service went on over his grave I was somehow reminded of the lovely cemetery at Lisbon where another English man of letters lies in a tomb far from his own country. I speak of Fielding.

I left Thérèse and Madame Espinel still at St. Christophe, and did not see them again before starting for England. They, I knew, would probably return to Paris, or perhaps would go to relatives of theirs in Spain. I could help them no more, and by now I discovered that my winter journey, or perhaps even my short visit to the death-chamber of Henry Maitland, had given me some kind of pulmonary catarrh which in my over-wrought and nervous state seemed likely, perhaps, to result in something more serious. Therefore, having done all that could be done, and having seen him put in the earth, I returned home hurriedly. On reaching England I was very ill for many days, but recovered without any serious results. Soon afterwards some one, I know not who it was, sent me a paragraph published in a religious paper which claimed Maitland as a disciple of the Church, for it said that he had died " in the fear of God's holy name, and with the comfort and strength of the Catholic faith." When some men die there are for ever crows and vultures about. Although very loath to say anything which would raise an angry discussion, I felt that this could not be passed by and that he would not have wished it to be passed by. Had he not written of a certain character in one of his books " that he should be buried as a son of the Church, to which he had never belonged, was a matter of indignation " ? That others felt as I did is proved by a letter I got from his friend Edmund Roden, who wrote to me : " You have seen the report that the ecclesiastical buzzards have got hold of Henry Maitland *in articulo mortis* and dragged him into the fold." [1]

My own views upon religion did not matter. They were stronger and more pronounced, and, it may be, more atheistical than his own. Nevertheless I knew what he felt about these things, and in consequence wrote the following letter to the editor of the paper which had claimed him for the Church : " My attention has been drawn to a statement in your columns that Henry Maitland died in communion with the Church of England, and I shall be much obliged if you will give to this contradiction the same publicity you granted, without investigation, to the calumny. I was intimate with Maitland for thirty years, and had every opportunity of noting his attitude towards all theological speculation. He not only accepted none of the dogmas formulated in the creeds and articles of the Church of England, but he considered it impossible that any Church's definition of the undefinable could have any significance for any intelligent man. During the whole of our long intimacy I never knew him to waver from that point of view.

" What communication may have reached you from any one who visited Maitland during his illness I do not know. But I presume you do not maintain that a change in his theological standpoint can reasonably be inferred from any words which he may have been induced to speak in a condition in which, according to the law of every civilised country, he would have been incompetent to sign a codicil to his will.

" The attempt to draw such a deduction will seem

[1] For Wells's more temperate explanation of this incident, see *Introduction*, p. 6.

dishonest to every fair-minded man ; and I rely upon your courtesy to publish this vindication of the memory of an honest and consistent thinker which you have, however unintentionally, aspersed."

Of course this letter was refused publication. The editor answered it in a note in which he maintained the position that the paper had taken up, stating that he was thoroughly satisfied with the sources of his information. I knew what those sources were and wrote a letter in anger to the chaplain of St. Pé, which, I fear, was full of very gross insults.

Seeing that the paper refused my letter admission to its columns, on the advice of certain other people I wrote to a London daily saying : " As the intimate friend of Henry Maitland for thirty years, I beg to state definitely that he had not the slightest intellectual sympathy with any creed whatsoever. From his early youth he had none, save for a short period when, for reasons other than intellectual, he inclined to a vague and nebulous Positivism. His mental attitude towards all theological explanations was more than critical, it was absolutely indifferent ; he could hardly understand how any one in the full possession of his faculties could subscribe to any formulated doctrines. No more than John Stuart Mill or Herbert Spencer could he have entered into communion with any Church."

Of course I knew, as any man must know who is acquainted with humanity and its frailties, that it was possible for Maitland, during the last few poisoned hours of his life, to go back in his delirium upon the whole of his previous convictions. He knew that he was dying. When he asked to know the truth he had been told it. In such circumstances some men break down. There are what people call death-bed repentances. Therefore I did my best to satisfy myself as to whether anything whatever had occurred which would give any colour to these theological lies. I could not trouble Thérèse upon this particular point, but it occurred to me that the nurse, who was a very intelligent woman, must be in a position to know something of the matter, and therefore wrote to her asking her to tell me all she knew. She replied to me about the middle of January, telling me that she had just then had a long talk with Mrs. Maitland, and giving me the following facts.

It appears that on Monday, December 21, Maitland was so ill that a consultation was deemed necessary, and that both the doctors agreed that it was impossible for the patient to live through the night, though in fact he did not die till nearly a week afterwards. On Thursday, December 24, the chaplain was sent for, not for any religious reasons, or because Maitland had called for him, but simply because Thérèse thought that he might find some pleasure in seeing an English face. When the clergyman came it did indeed have this effect, for Maitland's face lit up and he shook him heartily by the hand. At this moment the young doctor came in and told the clergyman privately that Maitland had no chance whatever, and that it was a wonder that he was still alive. It is quite certain that there was no religious conversation between the clergyman and the patient at this time. The nurse arrived at eleven o'clock on Sunday morning, and insisted on absolute quietness in the room. The clergyman simply peeped in at the door to say good-bye, for at that time Mr. Rivers was in charge in the bedroom.

The chaplain did not see Maitland again until the day I myself came to St. Christophe, when all was over. While Maitland was delirious it appears that he chanted some kind of *Te Deum* repeatedly. To what this was attributable no man can say with certainty, but it is a curious thing to reflect upon that " Basil " was concerned with the time of Gregory, and that Maitland had been studying most minutely the history of the early Church in many ecclesiastical works. According to those who heard his delirious talk, it seems that all he did say had reference to " Basil," the book about which he had been so anxious, and was never to finish. At any rate it is absolutely certain that Maitland never accepted, even in delirium, the offices of the Church before his death. Before I leave this matter I may mention that the chaplain complicated matters in no small degree before he retired from the scene, by declaring most disingenuously that he had not written the notice which appeared in print. Now this was perfectly true. He did not write it. He had asked a friend of his to do so. When he learnt the truth this friend very much regretted having undertaken the task. I understand that though the editor refused to withdraw this statement the authorities of the paper wrote to the chaplain in no pleased spirit after they had received my somewhat severely phrased communication. It is a sad and disagreeable subject, and I am glad to leave it.

# XIII

FOR ever on looking backwards one is filled with regrets, and one thing I regret greatly about Henry Maitland is that, though I might perhaps have purchased his little library, the books he had accumulated with so much joy and such self-sacrifice, I never thought of this until it was too late. Books made up so much of his life, and few of his had not been bought at the cost of what others would consider pleasure, or by the sacrifice of some sensation which he himself would have enjoyed at the time. Now I possess none of his books but those he gave me, save only the little " Anthologia Latina " which Thérèse herself sent to me. This was a volume in which he took peculiar delight, perhaps even more delight than he did in the Greek anthology, which I myself preferred so far as my Greek would then carry me. Many times I have seen him take down the little Eton anthology and read aloud. Now I myself may quote :

> *Animula, vagula, blandula,*
> *Hospes comesque corporis,*
> *Quæ nunc abibis in loca*
> *Pallidula, rigida, nudula——*

I believe his library was sold in Paris, for now that Thérèse had no settled home it was impossible to carry it about with her. Among these books were all those beautifully bound volumes which he had obtained as prizes at Moorhampton College, and others which he had picked up at various times in the various bookshops of London, so many of which he speaks of in " The

Meditations " [1]—his old Gibbon in quarto, and some hundreds of others chosen with joy because they appealed to him in a way only a book-lover can understand. He had a strange pleasure in buying old copies of the classics, which shows that he was perhaps after all more of a bookman than a scholar. He would have possessed such a copy of Lucretius as is on my own shelves, which has no notes but is wonderfully printed, rather than the newest edition by the newest editor. He was conscious that his chief desire was literature, not scholarship. Few indeed there are who know the classics as well as he did, who read them for ever with so much delight.

Maitland, for an Englishman, knew many languages. His Greek, though not extraordinarily deep, was most familiar. He could read Aristophanes lying on the sofa, thoroughly enjoying it, and rarely rising to consult Liddell and Scott, a book which he adored in the most odd fashion, perhaps because it knew so much Greek. There was no Latin author whom he could not read fluently. I took to him often a difficult passage in Juvenal and Persius, and rarely found him at fault, or slow to give me help. French he knew nearly as well as a Frenchman, and spoke it very fluently. His Italian was also good, and he spoke that too without hesitation. Spanish he only read ; I do not think he often attempted to speak it. " Don Quixote " in the original was a favourite book of his ; and his Italian can be judged by the fact that he read Dante's " Divina Commedia " almost as easily as Virgil. German too was an open book to him, and he had read most of the great men who wrote in it, understanding even the obscurities of " Titan." [2] I marked down the other day many of the books in which he chiefly delighted, or rather, let me say, many of the authors. Homer, of course, stood at the

[1] See *Henry Ryecroft :* " Spring," XII.          [2] By Jean Paul.

head of the list, for Homer he knew as well as he knew Shakespeare. He was a convinced Homeric unitarian, but here his conservative prejudices had their way. His adoration for Shakespeare was, perhaps, excessive, but the less said of that the better, for I have no desire to dilate on the general English over-estimation of that particular author. I do, however, understand how it was that Maitland worshipped him so, for whatever may be thought of Shakespeare's dramatic ability, or his characterisation, or his general psychology, there can be no dispute about his having been a master of " beautiful words." Milton he loved, and sometimes read his sonnets to me. Much of " Lycidas " he knew by heart, and some of " Il Penseroso." Among the Latins, Virgil, Catullus, and Tibullus were his favourites, although he took a curious interest in Cicero, a taste in which I was never able to follow him. I once showed to Maitland in the " Tusculan Disputations " what Cicero seemed to think a good joke. It betrayed such an extraordinary lack of humour that I was satisfied to leave the " Disputations " alone henceforth. The only Latin book which I myself introduced to Maitland was the " Letters " of Pliny. They afterwards became great favourites with him because some of them dealt with his beloved Naples and Vesuvius. Lucian's " Dialogues " he admired very much, finding them, as indeed they are, always delightful ; and it was very interesting to him when I showed him to what extent Disraeli was indebted to Lucian in those clever *jeux d'esprit* " Ixion in Heaven," " Popanilla," and " The Infernal Marriage." In the " Golden Ass " of Apuleius he knew the story of Psyche almost by heart. Petronius he read very frequently ; it contained some of the actual life of the old world. He knew Diogenes Laertius well, though he read that author, as Montaigne did, rather for the light he throws upon the private life of the Greeks than for the philosophy in the book ; and he frequently dipped into Athenæus the Deipnosophist. Occasionally, but very occasionally, he did read some ancient metaphysics, for Plato was a favourite of his—not, I think, on account of his philosophy, but because he wrote so beautifully. Aristotle he rarely touched, although he knew the " Poetics." He had a peculiar admiration for the Stoic Marcus Aurelius, in which I never followed him because the Stoic philosophy then seemed to me peculiarly inhuman. But, after all, among the Greeks his chief joy was the tragedians, and there was no single play or fragment of Æschylus, Sophocles, and Euripides that he did not know familiarly. Among the Frenchmen his great favourites were Rabelais and Montaigne and, later, Flaubert, Maupassant, Victor Hugo, Zola, Balzac, and the Goncourts. As I have said before, he had a great admiration for the Russian writers of eminence, and much regretted that he did not know Russian. Once he attempted it, but put it aside. I think Balzac was the only writer of importance that he read much of who did not possess a style ; he owned that he found him on that account at times almost impossible. Nevertheless he did read him, and learnt much from him ; but his chief admiration among the French on the ground of their artistry was for Flaubert and Maupassant. Zola's style did not appeal to him ; in fact in many of his books it is little better than Balzac's. Maitland's love of beautiful words and the rhythms of prose was as great as that of Meredith ; and no doubt his adoration of Shakespeare was founded on the fact that Shakespeare still remains the mighty enchanter in the world of phrases. He read English very deeply. There was little among the fields of English prose that he did not know well ; but again he loved best those who had a noble style of their own,

notably Sir Thomas Browne. If a man had something
to say and did not say it well, Maitland read him with
difficulty and held him at a discount. That is why he
loved Landor at his best, why he loved Meredith, and
why he often adored Hardy, especially in Hardy's earlier
works, before he began to " rail at the universe " and
disturb him. I think among other living writers of
English fiction I can hardly mention more than one of
whom he spoke with much respect, and he was Henry
James. As he was a conservative he was especially a
conservative critic. He found it difficult to appreciate
anything which was wholly new, and the rising school
of Celtic literature, which means much, and may mean
more, in English literature, did not appeal to him. He
lived in the past, even in English, and often went back to
Chaucer and drank at his well and at the everlasting
fountain of Malory. So, as I have said, he loved old
Walton. Boswell he read yearly at least, for he had an
amazing admiration for old Johnson, a notable truth-
teller. The man who could say what he thought, and
say it plainly, was ever his favourite, although I could
never induce him to admire Machiavelli, for the coldness
of Machiavelli's intellect was a little too much for him.
The pure intellect never appealed to Maitland. I think
if he had attempted " The Critique of Pure Reason " he
would have died before he had learnt Kant's vocabulary.
Yet I once gave him a copy of it in the original which I
could not read myself. The only very modern writer
that he took to was Walt Whitman, and the trouble I had
in getting him to see anything there was amazing,
though at last he succumbed and was characteristically
enthusiastic.

What he wanted in literature was emotion, feeling,
and humour—literature that affected him sensuously,
and made him happy, and made him forget. When one

looks back at his books it is strange to think how much he loved pure beauty, though he found himself compelled to write, only too often, of the sheer brutality of modern civilisation and the foulest life of London. Yet by nature he loved satire, and his own mind was essentially in some ways satiric. His greatest gift was perhaps that of irony, which he frequently exercised at the expense of his public. I remember very well his joy when something he had written which was ironically intended from the first word to the last was treated seriously by the critics. He was reminded, as he indeed reminded me, of Samuel Butler's " Fairhaven," that book on Christianity which was reviewed by one great religious paper as an essay in religious apologetics. This recalls to my mind the fact that I have forgotten to say how much he admired Samuel Butler's books, or those with which he was more particularly acquainted, " Erewhon " and " Erewhon Revisited." Anything which dug knives into the gross stupidity of the mass of English opinion afforded him the intensest gratification. If it attacked their religion or their vanity he was equally delighted, and when it came to their hypocrisy—in spite of the defence of English hypocrisy made later in " The Meditations " [1]—he was equally pleased. In this connection I am reminded of a very little incident of no particular importance which occurred to him when he was upon one occasion at the Royal Academy. That year Sir Frederick Leighton exhibited a fine decorative panel of a nude figure. While Maitland was looking at it a typical English matron with three young flappers of daughters passed him. One of the girls stood in front of this nude and said, " Oh, mamma, what is this ? " Whereupon her mother replied hurriedly, " Only a goddess, my dear, only a goddess ! Come along—only a

[1] *Henry Ryecroft :* " Winter," XX.

goddess." And he quoted to himself and afterwards to me, from "Roman Women" : "And yet I love you not, nor ever can, Distinguished woman on the Pincian ! " If I remember rightly, the notable address to Englishwomen in T. E. Brown's poem was published separately in a magazine [1] which I brought to him. It gave great occasion for chuckling.

I have not attempted to give any complete catalogue of all Maitland's reading, but think what has been said will indicate its reach. What he desired was to read the best that had been written in all western languages ; and very few men have read so much, although he made, in some ways, but little use of it. Nevertheless this life among books was his true life. Among books he lived, and among them he would have died. Had any globe-trotting Gillman offered to show him the world, he would have declined, I think, to leave the littoral of the Mediterranean, though with a book-loving Gillman he might have explored all literature.

[1] The *New Review*, August 1895.

# XIV

THERE have been few men so persecuted by Fortune as to lead lives of unhappiness, lighted only by transient gleams of the sun, who are yet pursued beyond the grave by outcries and misfortune, but this was undoubtedly the case with Maitland. Of course he always had notable ill luck, but it sprang from his nature as well as from the nature of things. When a man puts himself into circumstances to which he is equal he may have misfortunes, and sometimes disasters, but he has not perpetual adversity. Maitland's nature was for ever thrusting him into positions of which he was not master. His disposition, his very heredity, seems to have invited trouble. So out of his first great calamity sprang all the rest. He had not been equal to the stress laid upon him, and in later life he was never equal to the stress he laid upon himself. That is what ill luck is : an instinctive lack of wisdom.[1]

His ill luck began early. It lasted even beyond the grave. Some men have accounted it a calamity to have a biography written of them. The first who said so must have been English, for in this country the absence of biographic art is rendered the more peculiarly dreadful by the existence in our language of one or two masterpieces. In some ways I would now very willingly cease to speak, for nearly all is written that was in my mind, and I have spoken nothing which is not truly in his defence. As I declared in the very first chapter, he

[1] Here, in the first edition, follows a longish passage dealing with Gissing's health. Roberts omitted it from his revised, 1923, edition ; and there seems no good reason to restore here what the author then decided to expunge.

had an earnest desire that if anything were written about him after his death it should be really true. Still there are some things yet to be put down, especially about " Basil " and its publication. He left this book unfinished : it lacked some few chapters dealing with the final catastrophe. It fell to the executors to arrange for the publication of the incomplete book. As Maitland had left no money, certainly not that two thousand pounds for which he vainly hoped, there were still his children to consider ; and it was thought necessary, for reasons I do not appreciate, to get a preface written for the book with a view, which seemed to me idle, of procuring it a great sale.

It appears that Rivers offered to write this preface if it were wanted. What he wrote was afterwards published separately.[1] The executors did not approve it, again for reasons which I do not appreciate, for on the whole it was an admirable piece of work. Yet I do not believe Rivers was sincere in the view he took of " Basil " as a work of art. In later years he acknowledged as much, but he thought it was his duty to say everything that could possibly be said with a view to imposing it on a reluctant public. In this article the passage mainly objected to was that which speaks obscurely of his early life at Moorhampton College, and refers as obscurely to his initial great disaster. The reference was needed, and could hardly be avoided. Rivers said nothing openly but referred to " an abrupt, incongruous reaction and collapse." This no doubt excited curiosity in certain people, but seeing that so many already knew the truth, I cannot perceive what was to be gained by entire silence. However, this preface was rejected and Mr. Harold Edgeworth was asked to write another. This he did, but it was a frigid performance. The writer

[1] *Monthly Review*, August, 1904.

acknowledged his ignorance of much that Maitland had written, and avowed his want of sympathy with most of it.

Naturally enough, the trouble growing out of this dispute gave rise to considerable comment. As some theological buzzards had dropped out of a murky sky upon Maitland's corpse, so some literary kites now found a subject to gloat upon. Nevertheless the matter presently passed. " Basil " unhappily, was no success ; and if one must speak the truth, it was rightly a failure. It is curious and bitter to reflect that when he was dealing at the last in some kind of peace and quiet with the one chosen subject, that he had thought of for so many years and prepared for so carefully, it should by no means have proved what he believed it. There is, indeed, no such proof as " Basil " in the whole history of letters that the writer was not doing the work that his nature called for. Who that knows " Magna Græcia," and who, indeed, that ever spoke with him, will not feel that if he had visited one by one all the places that he mentions in this story, and had written about them and about the historical characters that he hoped to realise, the book might have been as great as or even greater than the shining pages of " Magna Græcia " ? It was in the consideration of these things, while reviving the aspects of the past that he felt so deeply and loved so much, that his native and natural genius shone. In fiction it was only when rage and anger and disgust inspired him that he could hope to equal anything of the passion which he felt about his temperamental and proper work. Those books in which he let himself go perfectly naturally, and those books which came out of him as a terrible protest against modern civilisation, are alone great. Yet it is hard to speak without emotion and without pain of " Basil." He

believed in it so greatly, and yet believed in it no more
than any writer must while he is at work.  The artist's
own illusion of a book's strength and beauty is necessary to
any accomplishment.  He must believe with faith or do
nothing.  Maitland failed because it was not his real work.

In one sense the great books of his middle period
were what writers and artists know as " pot-boilers."
They were, indeed, written for an actual living, for bread
and for cheese and occasionally a very little butter.
But they had to be written.  He was obliged to do something, and did these best ; he could do no other.  He
was always in exile.  That was the point in my mind
when I wrote one long article about him in a promising
but passing magazine which preened its wings in Bond
Street and died before the end of its first month.  This
article was called " The Exile of Henry Maitland." [1]
There is something of the same feeling in much that has
been written of him by men perhaps better qualified in
many ways than myself had they known him as well.
I have spoken of the able criticism Thomas Sackville
wrote of him in the preface to the book of short stories[2]
which was published after Maitland's death.  In the
*Fortnightly Review* Edwin Warren [3] wrote a feeling and
sympathetic article about him.  Jacob Levy [4] wrote not
without discernment of the man.  And of one thing all
these writers seemed tolerably sure, that in himself
Maitland stood alone.  But he only stood alone in the
best work of his middle period.  And even that work
was alien from his native mind.

In an early article written about him while he yet
lived I said that he occupied a high and solitary place,
because he belonged to no school, and most certainly

[1] *The Exile of George Gissing*, in *Albany*, Christmas 1904.
[2] *The House of Cobwebs*, 1906.
[3] Arthur Waugh (*Fortnightly Review*, February 1904).
[4] Perhaps Morris Colles (*Academy*, January 1904).

not to any English school. It was impossible to imitate, and no one could truly even caricature him. One great characteristic of his best work was that he founded it on deep and accurate knowledge and keen observation. Yet its power lay in a bent, in a mood of mind, not by any means in any subject, even though his satiric discussion of what he called the " ignobly decent " showed his strength, and, indirectly, his inner character. His very repugnance to his early subjects led him to choose them. He showed what he wished the world to be by declaring and proving that it possessed every conceivable opposite to his desires. It was pointed out some time ago, but may be insisted upon again, that in one sense he manifested an instinctive affinity for the lucid and subtle Tourgeniev. There is no more intensely depressing book in the entire English language than " Isabel." The hero's desires reached to the stars, but he was not able to steal or take so much as a farthing rushlight. Not even Demetri Roudine, that futile essence of futility, equals this, Maitland's literary child of bitter unable ambitions. These Russians indeed were the writers with whom Maitland had most sympathy. They moved what Zola had never been able to stir in him, for he was never a Zolaist either in mind or method. No man without a style could really influence him for more than a moment. Even his beloved Balzac, fecund and insatiable, had no lasting hold upon him, much as he admired the man's ambitions, his unparalleled industry, his mighty construction. For Balzac was truly architectonic, even if barbarous, though his constructions are often imaginary and his perspectives a blotted mystery. But great construction is obviously alien from Maitland. He wanted no elaborate architecture to do his thinking in. He would have been contented in a porch, or preferably in a cloister.

I have declared that his greatest book is " The Exile "—I mean his greatest book among his novels. To say it is a masterpiece is for once not to abuse the word ; it is intense, deeply psychological, moving, true. " *L'anatomia presuppone il cadavere*," says Gabriele D'Annunzio, but " The Exile " is intolerable and wonderful vivisection. Yet men do bleed and live, and the protagonist in this book—in much, in very much, Henry Maitland—bleeds but will not die. He was born out of the leisured classes and resented it with an incredible bitterness, with a bitterness unparalleled in literature. I know that on one occasion Maitland spoke to me with a certain joy of somebody who had written to him about his books and had selected " The Exile " as the greatest of them. I think he knew it was great. It was, naturally, an ineffable failure from the commercial point of view.

On more than one occasion, as it was known that I was acquainted with Maitland, men asked me to write about him. I never did so without asking his permission. This happened once in 1895. He answered me : " What objection could I possibly have, unless it were that I should not like to hear you reviled for log-rolling ? But it seems to me that you might well write an article which would incur no such charge ; and indeed, by so doing, you would render me a very great service. For I have in mind at present a careful and well-written attack in the current *Spectator*. Have you seen it ? Now I will tell you what my feelings are about this frequent attitude in my critics."

Maitland's views upon critics and reviewing were often somewhat astounding. He resented their folly very bitterly. Apropos of a review of one man's books [1] he wrote : " I have also, unfortunately, seen the ——.

---

[1] The first edition reads : " one of Rivers's books."

Now, can you tell me (in moments of extreme idleness one wishes to know such things) who the people are who review fiction for the ——? Are they women, soured by celibacy, and by ineffectual attempts to succeed as authors? Even as they treat you this time they have consistently treated me—one continuous snarl and sneer. They are beastly creatures—I can think of no other term."

It was unfortunate that he took these things seriously, for nobody knows so well as the reviewers that their work is rarely serious. Yet, according to them the general effect of Maitland's books, especially " Jubilee," [1] was false, misleading, and libellous, and in essence caricature. One particular critic spoke of the " brutish stupefaction of his men and women," and said, " his realism inheres only in his rendering of detail." Now Maitland declared that the writer exhibited a twofold ignorance—first of the life he depicted, and again of the books in which he depicted it. Maitland went on to say : " He—the critic—speaks specially of ' Jubilee,' so for the moment we will stick to that. I have selected from the great mass of lower middle-class life a group of people who repre- sent certain of its grossnesses, weaknesses, etc., peculiar to our day. Now in the first place, this group of people, on its worst side, represents a degradation of which the critic has obviously no idea. In the second place, my book, if properly read, contains abundant evidence of good feeling and right thinking in those members of the group who are not hopelessly base. Pass to instances : ' The seniors live a . . . life unglorified by a single fine emotion or elevating instinct.' Indeed ? What about Mr. Ward,[2] who is there precisely to show that there can be, and are, these emotions and instincts in individuals ? Of the young people (to say not a word

[1] *In the Year of Jubilee* (1894).          [2] Mr. Lord

about Nancy, at heart an admirable woman), how is it possible to miss the notes of fine character in poor Halley ? [1]  Is not the passionate love of one's child an ' elevating instinct ' ?  nor yet a fine emotion ?  Why, even Nancy's brother shows at the end that favourable circumstances could bring out in him gentleness and goodness."

There indeed spoke Maitland.  He felt that everything was circumstance, and that for nine hundred and ninety-nine out of a thousand circumstance was truly too much, as it had been for him.  It appears that the critic added that the general effect of the novel was false ; and Maitland replied that it would be so to a very rapid skimmer of the book, precisely as the general effect upon a rapid observer of the people themselves would be false.  He was enraged to think that, though people thought it worth while to write at length about his books, they would not take the trouble to study them seriously.  He added : " In this section of the lower middle class the good is not on the surface ; neither will it be found on the surface of my narrative."

In this letter he went on to say something more of his books in general.  Apropos of a paragraph written by Mr. Glass about his work as a whole, he said : " My books deal with people of many social strata ; there are the vile working class, the aspiring and capable working class, the vile lower middle, the aspiring and capable lower middle, and a few representatives of the upper middle class.  My characters range from the vileness of 'Arry Parsons to the genial and cultured respectability of Mr. Comberbatch.  There are books as disparate as ' The Under-World ' and ' The Unchosen.'  But what I desire to insist upon is this, that the most characteristic,

[1] Peachey.

the most important, part of my work is that which deals with a class of young men distinctive of our time—well-educated, fairly bred, *but without money*. It is this fact, as I gather from reviews and conversation, of the poverty of my people which tells against their recognition as civilised beings. ' Oh,' said some one to Butler, ' do ask Mr. Maitland to make his people a little better off.' There you have it."

And there one has also the source of Maitland's fountain of bitterness. He went on to say : " Now think of some of these young men, Hendon,[1] Gifford[2] Medwin,[3] Pick,[4] Early,[5] Hillward,[6] Mallow.[7] Do you mean to say that books containing such a number of such men deal, first and foremost, with the commonplace and the sordid ? Why, these fellows are the very reverse of commonplace ; most of them are martyred by the fact of possessing uncommon endowments. Is it not so ? This side of my work, to me the most important, I have never yet seen recognised. I suppose Glass would class these men as ' at best genteel, and not so very genteel.' Why, 'ods bodikins ! there's nothing in the world so hateful to them as gentility. But you know all this, and can you not write of it rather trenchantly ? I say nothing about my women. That is a moot point. But surely there are some of them who help to give colour to the groups I draw." The end of the letter was : " I write with a numbed hand. I haven't been warm for weeks. This weather crushes me. Let me have a line about this letter."

The sort of poverty which crushed the aspiring is the

[1] Possibly Hubert Eldon (*Demos*).
[2] Biffen (*New Grub Street*).
[3] Probably Milvain (*Ibid.*).
[4] Peak (*Born in Exile*).
[5] Possibly Langley (*Sleeping Fires*), or Otway (*The Crown of Life*).
[6] Hilliard (*Eve's Ransom*).
[7] Probably Mallard (*The Emancipated*).

keynote to the best work he did. He knew it, and was right in knowing it. He played all these parts himself. In many protean forms Maitland is discerned under the colour and character of his chosen names ; and so far as he depicted a class hitherto untouched, or practically untouched, in England, as he declares, he was a great writer of fiction. But he was not a romantic writer. There were some books of romance he loved greatly. Often and often we spoke of Murger's " Vie de Bohème." I do not think there was any passage in that book which so appealed to him as when Rodolphe worked in his adventitious fur-coat in his windy garret, declaring genially : " Maintenant le thermomètre va être furieuse-ment vexé." Nevertheless there is no doubt that he knew, and few knew so well, the very bitter truth that Murger only vaguely indicated here and there in scattered passages. In the " Vie de Bohème " these characters " range " themselves at last ; but mostly such men did not. They went under, they died in the hospital, they poisoned themselves, they blew out their brains, they sank and became degraded parasites of an uncomprehending bourgeoisie.

I spoke some time ago of the painful hour when Maitland came to me to declare his considered opinion that I myself could not write successful fiction. No doubt he was correct, though he was correct for other reasons than those he gave. It is odd that I never returned the compliment, for though I knew he could, and did, write great fiction, I knew his best work in other circumstances would not have been fiction. Out of martyrdom may come great things, but not out of martyrdom spring the natural blossoms of the natural mind. That he lived in the devil's twilight between the Dan of Camberwell and the Beersheba of Camden Town, when his natural environment should have been

Italy, Rome, or Sorrento, is an unfading tragedy. Only once or twice in his life did a spring or summer come to him in which he might grow the flowers he loved best and knew to be his natural destiny. The greatest tragedy of all, to my mind, is that final tragedy of " Basil " in which at last, after long years of toil in fiction while fiction was yet necessary to his livelihood, he was compelled by his training to put into the form of a novel a theme not fit for such treatment save in the hands of a native and easy story-teller.

I have said nothing, or little except by implication, of the man's style. In many ways it was notable and even noble. To such a literary intelligence, informed with all the learning of the past towards which he leant, much of his style was inevitable ; it was the man and his own. For the greater part it is lucid rather than sparkling, clear, if not cold ; yet with a subdued rhythm, the result of much Latin and more Greek, for the metres of the Greek tragedies always inspired him with their noble cadences. Though he was often bitter, especially in his employment of irony, of which he is the only complete master in English literature besides Samuel Butler, he could rise to heights of passionate description ; for here and there a sense of luxury tinges his words with Tyrian purple—and this in spite of all his sense of restraint, which was more marked than that of almost any living writer.

When I think of it all, and consider his partly wasted years, it is a matter of wonder how it was that he induced himself to deal with the life he knew so well ; but while the commercialism exists which he abhorred as much as he abhorred the society in which it flourishes, there seems no other practicable method for a poor man of letters to attain speech and yet to live. I often declared that fiction as we wrote it was truly diagnostic of a disordered and unnecessarily degraded form of civilisation ; and he replied with deep feeling that to him the idylls of Theocritus, of Moschus, the simple tragedies, the natural woes and joys of men who ploughed the soil or worked at the wine-press, were the truest and most vivid forms and subjects of Art. Neither before his death nor after did he attain the artist's true and great reward of recognition in the full sense that would have satisfied him even if he had remained in poverty. Nevertheless there were some who knew. There are perhaps a few more who know now that he is gone and cannot hear them. Popularity he never hoped for, and never will attain, but he has a secure place in the hierarchy of the literature of England which he loved. He appeals now as he appealed while he lived, not to the idle and the foolish, not to the fashionable mob, but to the more august tribunal of those who have the sympathy that comes from understanding.

THE END

# Appendices

# Appendix A

## PREFACE TO FIRST EDITION 1912

THIS book was dictated by J. H. mostly in my presence, and I consider it well worth publishing. No doubt Henry Maitland is not famous, though since his death a great deal has been written of him. Much of it, outside of literary criticism, has been futile, false, and uninstructed. But J. H. really knew the man, and here is what he said of him. We shall be told, no doubt, that we have used Maitland's memory for our own ends. Let that be as it may ; when there is no proof of guilt, there may well be none of innocence. The fact remains that Henry Maitland's life was worth doing, even in the abbreviated and censored form in which it now appears. The man was not eminent, only because he was not popular and did not live long enough. One gets to eminence nowadays by longevity, self-praise, or bad work. While Maitland starved, X or Y or Z might wallow in a million sixpences. In this almost childishly simple account of a man's life there is the essence of a literary epoch. Here is a writing man put down, crudely it may be, but with a certain power. There is no book quite like it in the English tongue, and the critic may take what advantage he will of that opening for his wit.

At any rate we have a portrait emerging which is real. Henry Maitland stands on his feet, and on his living feet. He is not a British statue done in the best mortuary manner. There is far too little sincere biography in English. We are a mealy-mouthed race, hypocrites by the grave and the monument. Ten words of natural eulogy, and another ten of curious and sympathetic comment, may be better than tons of marble built up by a hired liar with his tongue in his cheek. In the whole book, which cannot be published now, there are things worth waiting for. I have cut and retrenched with pain, for I wanted to risk the whole, but no writer or editor is his own master in England. I am content to have omitted some truth if I have permitted nothing false. The reader who can say truly, " I should not have liked to meet Henry Maitland," is a fool or a fanatic, or more probably both. Neither of those who are primarily responsible for this little book is answerable to such. We do not desire his praise, or even his mere allowance. All who are interested in the art of letters and those who practise in the High Court of Literature, will perceive what we had in our minds. Here is life, not a story or a constructed diary, and the art with which it is done is a secondary matter. If Henry Maitland bleeds and howls, so did Philoctetes, and the outcry of Henry Maitland is most pertinent to our lives. For all life, even at its best, is tragic ; and there is much in Maitland's which is dramatically common to our world as we see it and live in it. If we have lessened him at times from the point of view of a hireling in biographic praise, we have set him down life size all the same ; and as we ask for no praise, we care for no blame. Here is the man.

MORLEY ROBERTS [1]

[1] Morley Roberts, in his first edition of the book, ended this Preface with the following Note : " The full manuscript, which may possibly be published after some years, is, in the meantime, placed in safe custody." Whether this was added to give a touch of verisimilitude, or whether in fact such manuscript ever existed, or still exists, is matter for conjecture.

# *Appendix B*

## PREFACE TO REVISED EDITION 1923

THIS book has been gone over mainly from the literary point of view as, owing to illness when it was first issued, none of the slips and repetitions which inevitably occur during rapid dictation was corrected in the proofs. Two or three notes have been added as well as an appendix upon some new matter which came from Chicago. A few paragraphs which now seem unnecessary have been removed, but the book remains substantially what it was, still as rough, perhaps, as a hasty sketch in clay, but not without life and rude vigour, although it may show the modeller's very finger marks and therefore lack finish, as it must necessarily lack finality.

MORLEY ROBERTS

## Appendix C

### MAITLAND'S LIFE IN CHICAGO [1]

THE references to obscure early work, done in Chicago during this desperate spring of 1877, led to a search among the files of the *Tribune* by two journalists, Mr. Vincent Starrett and Mr. Christopher Hagerup. Although friends, they undertook the task independently and without each other's knowledge, in spite of the fact that they met at regular intervals, even as Maitland and I did, for enthusiastic talks about famous English writers. Such enthusiasm, and it does exist in America, is really the greatest remaining bond between this country and the United States. It is the one thing in which the open or concealed divergencies and even hostilities of national relations do not act. Luck in the search fell to Hagerup, with whom, as with Starrett, I was then corresponding. Hagerup wrote to me in a letter dated September 22, 1916 : " I continued my search of the *Tribune* files and have, I believe, been abundantly rewarded, and your dates verify my belief that I have found four of his stories. I should hesitate as to the first two, but if he admitted they were ' mere sentimental tosh,' it clinches my belief that they are his." It seems that the last two stories were signed with Maitland's three true initials, the middle one of which, R., he afterwards discarded.[2] Hagerup said, truly enough, that all four tales resembled each other in having three divisions and a characteristic outlook. This matter of three divisions seems to me interesting, as it indicates at a very early period the tendencies of a writer with a nascent sense of form. Years later he and I often discussed form with reference to Aristotle's well-known analysis of tragedy into seeds, growth, climax, catastrophe and close, an analysis much to be commended to many writers, not all of them young, who nowadays seem to think that an amorphous botch of sentimental indecency, or a laboured defence of their own

[1] First included in the revised edition of 1923.
[2] His full name was George Robert Gissing.

proclivities, can be a work of art. Hagerup continued : " I can find only four, though more may be discovered on closer search. They appeared as follows :

March 10, 1877, ' The Sins of the Fathers.'
March 31, 1877, ' R.I.P.'
April 14, 1877, ' Too Dearly Bought.'
May 12, 1877, ' Gretchen.'

"Just as soon as I get them in manuscript I shall send them to you for your opinion."

What my opinion was I will give later, but I think that the enthusiasm and perseverance of these men deserves a few more lines. Starrett was as gratified by his friend's success as he would have been by his own, and everything he wrote to me showed a very happy passion, not only for Maitland, but for literature generally. If I seem to insist on this it is because it is not so rare in America as some English circles imagine. Starrett said : " I know Hagerup . . . but when I wrote to you I had not heard of his success. Shortly after I mailed your letter he told me of his triumph, and I was as pleased as he. . . . I miss him, as we used to discuss ' Maitland ' and Meredith at least once a week." Shortly after this Hagerup wrote to me again. He said of his friend : " We have had fortnightly visits and talked of first editions, he presenting the most interesting tales of young poets who are ' on the way ' or who have died and been forgotten. I, of course, sang the praise of Meredith and ' Maitland,' and presented Starrett with a copy of your ' Life of Henry Maitland,' which was full of notes I had gathered. I suppose this is what suggested to him the perusal of the *Tribune* files. It is a matter of gratification to me that I found the stories, even though my rival is so good a friend. I did not know he was searching for them until after I told him that the stories were found."

There was some suggestion made that these tales should be re-published privately in a limited edition, but when I considered what the writer thought of them and pondered over the common literary vice of reprinting every scrap which a self-respecting author condemns to the waste-paper basket, it seemed inadvisable to do so. There would be a much brighter opinion generally of such poets as Herrick, say, if no more than the poems worthy of an anthology had been preserved.

" To Julia " is worth ten thousand epigrams, and Herrick, or
Blake, or Keats on Olympus must curse their earthly editors
in chorus.  No doubt there can be found, in the tales from
the *Tribune* if not " la griffe de l'aigle," at least signs of some
of the main motives which afterwards characterised the full
flood of better work.  Hagerup, indeed, remarked to me,
" through all the stories there is, even so early, that characteristic strain of sympathy for the cultured gentleman who doesn't
exactly fit his environment."  I may note here, before leaving
this part of the subject, that Maitland appears to have had
a permanent influence on the *Chicago Tribune*.  From the time
he suggested fiction to the editor stories regularly appear.
Among the writers who followed him was Bret Harte.

I do not propose to criticise the four tales at length, but as
I trust they will not be re-published [1] a few words about them
may be permitted.  I find no phrases which suggest the merit
of the later writings.  It may be fancy, but they appear
anything but youthful, as they seem the work of a depressed
oldish man, not unaccustomed to writing, rather than that of
a young one.  Their schemes lack original invention.  Maitland
drew on his memory and out of ancient hackneys got no new
paces.  In " The Sins of the Fathers " a young man helps a
girl whom he finds in poverty and despair, and it is in the
first sentence only that one discerns a faint suggestion of the
kind of milieu he afterwards in some books made his own.
" A broad archway, the gloom of its chill murky shadow only
deepened by the flicker of the shattered gas-lamp," gives a
certain promise soon disappointed by the purest conventionality.
The hero, son of a rich manufacturer, finds a girl in distress
and gets her work, falls in love with her, and asks for his
parent's leave to marry her.  This is naturally enough refused,
but the cunning father takes the girl into his own house and
sends his son to America to make his own living and show
that he can do so.  The young fellow takes to teaching and
soon hears that the girl he left behind in England is dead.
This is, of course, not true.  The father has caused a letter to
be forged by which the girl is set free by her apparently in-
constant lover.  The hero soon falls in love again and marries
in America, now with his father's consent, and while at the

[1] But of course they have been, in America, in 1924 : *Sins of the Fathers and
Other Tales.*

theatre with his wife recognises, and is recognised by, the girl he thought dead, who is on the New York stage as a chorus girl. He manages to send his wife home and waits outside the stage door for the heroine, who falls on his neck but suddenly becomes mad on hearing that he has married. She urges him to spend an hour with her and leads him not to her rooms, but to the river, then slightly frozen over. She seizes hold of him and plunges with him into the water and both are drowned. So, quite irrelevantly, " the sins of the fathers are visited on the children."

This is really intolerable, but here and there we find a few small signs of H.M. He heartily approves of the hero's wife because she was scrupulously neat and a good housekeeper. His later lamentations on such subjects had a deep root in him.

The second, unsigned story, " R.I.P.," is equally the product of rat-riddled convention combined with the result of reading some French romances. The scene is laid in an ancient town under the shadow of the Pyrenees, although he had then never been in France. When reading it I wondered if he ever re-membered, when living within sight of La Rhune and Las Tres Coronas, his Chicagoan description of the " crazy old houses on each side of the narrow crooked streets, in which it would occasion no surprise to suddenly meet two of the monks of Rabelais or the knights of Froissart." We may note without surprise the split infinitive, later a thing to anger him as much as a nominativus pendens, or that curse of modern English, the use of " like " for " as." The story is of the simplest. A beautiful lady comes to the old inn, dismisses her driver, and next day is found dead, clad in rich raiment, a " veil of exquisite fabric," and gold bracelets, " set with priceless jewels." Naturally enough there is a letter, with a purse of gold, which gives directions that she is to be buried just as she was found. This appears to have been done without any *post-mortem* larceny, or any interference by the French authorities, who appear to have lost a great opportunity. At a later period Maitland would have sought legal accuracy at any cost. Years afterwards a wanderer sits by her tomb, and on learning the story betrays agitation, and is led to relate his own tale to the ancient innkeeper. An aristocrat, he had fallen in love with a very beautiful peasant, and married her

to the rage of his brother, the presumptive heir. On the day
of the marriage another woman, bribed by the brother tells
the bride that *she* is the real wife. The credulous young
woman therefore runs away and commits suicide, while her
unhappy husband deserts his estates, leaves them to the villain,
and seeks his wife the wide world over. I find nothing in
this suggestive of the writer but its curious lack of passionate
resentment and revenge. Most men would have seen to it that
such a brother inherited nothing but the nearest grave. That,
however, was never Maitland's way.

The third story, signed with the three initials, is called " Too
Dearly Bought," and is to some extent a reminiscence of " The
Old Curiosity Shop," at any rate so far as it concerns the little
girl, who fades away somewhat in the style of Little Nell. The
theme is that of an old cobbler who robs his benefactor of
ten pounds to take his grandchild to see the country. He goes
back to his native village and, when the child dies, repents
and sets to work to make enough to repay the forced loan.
He does so after years, and going back to London restores the
money and dies at once. The whole performance is to the
last degree painful to such as remember their early efforts to
compose a consecutive story, a feat natural to few and
absolutely alien from Maitland's mind. It seems possible to
hear the wretched author's groans, suppressed though they
must have been by the near neighbourhood of the wasters
collected in his miserable lodging. It can be seen from
Maitland's later more successful sketches that he lacked the
capacity for the popular *conte*, and the bitter necessity for such
premature work must nearly have driven him mad. He
wanted space and time to work in.

The last story is on a level with the others. A rich young
dilettante painter falls in love with a picture, " Gretchen at
the Spinning Wheel," and seeks the original model. He finds
her by one of the coincidences with which young artists and
many old ones save a narrative from natural and deserved
extinction, and, after a sad interval in which he believes her
married, marries her himself. A few signs of French reading
can be detected. One sentence goes : " He passed his days
in an agreeable manner, now amusing himself in his elegant
atelier, now visiting his numerous friends and acquaintances."

It may be doubted if there is any real mark of the author

in any of these tales beyond a tendency to a certain objective realism and his sympathy with those who have " seen better days." They are not more worth printing than Blake's abuse of Sir Joshua Reynolds or poor Hayley, and those who admire his best work will think no more of them. If the first step costs most to the worker, it may be worth nothing to others. All the same I think they may be mentioned, if only to show how difficult from the very beginning the writing of fiction was to Maitland.

# Index of Recurring Pseudonyms

## PEOPLE AND PLACES

# TITLES OF BOOKS

| | |
|---|---|
| Basil | Veranilda |
| Best of All Things, The | The Crown of Life |
| | |
| Children of the Dawn | Workers in the Dawn |
| | |
| Exile, The | Born in Exile |
| | |
| Isabel | Isabel Clarendon |
| | |
| Magna Græcia | By the Ionian Sea |
| Meditations of Mark Sumner, The | The Private Papers of Henry Ryecroft |
| Mob, The | Demos |
| Morning ; or In the Morning | A Life's Morning |
| | |
| Outside the Pale | The Unclassed |
| | |
| Paternoster Row | New Grub Street |
| Purification, The | The Purification of Dolores Silva |
| | |
| Rachel | Rachel Marr |
| | |
| Unchosen, The | The Odd Women |
| Under-World, The | The Nether World |
| | |
| Victorian Novelists | Charles Dickens : a Critical Study |
| Vortex, The | The Whirlpool |
| | |
| Western Trail, The | The Western Avernus |

MADE AND PRINTED IN GREAT BRITAIN BY
MORRISON AND GIBB LIMITED, LONDON AND EDINBURGH